THE
EDUCATION
OF THE
SCIENTIST
IN A
FREE
SOCIETY

Papers delivered at a conference
commemorating the 50th Anniversary
of the Marquette University
College of Engineering
May 20 21 and 22 1959

THE MARQUETTE UNIVERSITY PRESS 1959

A. Bernard Drought

INTRODUCTION

THE Marquette University College of Engineering commemorated the 50th Anniversary of its founding during the year 1959. As a major part of this celebration the College sponsored an academic conference dealing with problems surrounding "The Education of the Scientist in a Free Society." Members of the Marquette faculty, distinguished scholars from other universities, and leaders in various fields participated in this three-day conference, held May 20, 21 and 22, 1959.

Traditionally, American scholars have maintained that one of the essentials of the truly free society is the education of free, intelligent men. American universities, each in its own fashion, have sought to become communities of scholars dedicated to a pursuit of truth aimed at achieving the highest measure of human freedom.

Today this traditional American concept has been doubly challenged. First, the exploding advances of science creating the techno-

A. Bernard Drought is Dean, College of Engineering, Marquette University and chairman of the faculty planning committee for this conference.

logical age have projected the highly trained specialist in the field of science into a position of prominence in our society. Oftentimes today, decisions are made in the field of science—areas in which the traditionally educated man is often a stranger—which affect the lives and welfare of nations and the entire world. The ability of man to govern himself, to control his own destiny, has been seriously challenged.

Added to this is the even more frightening challenge of international Communism which has harnessed the achievements of science to the purpose of totalitarianism. The question of world survival will be answered in part by a nation's scientific achievements. The free society finds itself faced with the double problem of preserving individual freedom and national political existence.

The Marquette University College of Engineering sponsored this academic conference in the hope of disclosing the full complexity of this problem and of aiding in its solution. The four addresses which were delivered at sessions open to the general public appear first in this volume. They are followed by papers extracted from the panel discussions which summarized the proceedings of the conference. Participants in the discussion sessions included scientists, educators, and industrialists. It is regretted that it was not feasible to report in detail the frank yet objective discussions of the seminar groups.

Marquette University presents this volume in the hope that it may add to the understanding of some of the problems which surround the education of the scientist today.

The University is grateful to the following discussants who joined with the program speakers and with members of her faculty in the round-table discussion sessions: Clyde M. Brown, University of Wisconsin; R. B. Downs, University of Illinois Library; Lloyd C. Ferguson, Michigan State University; John Gammell, Allis Chalmers Mfg. Co.; Paul R. Goudy, Square D Company; Thomas J. Higgins, University of Wisconsin; Dumont F. Kenny, The National Conference of Christians and Jews; C. J. Nuesse, The Catholic University of America; Simon Ostrach, National Aeronautics and Space Administration; L. E. Saline, General Electric Company; Theodore N. Tahmisian, Argonne National Laboratory; Kurt F. Wendt, University of Wisconsin; and Karl O. Werwath, Milwaukee School of Engineering.

The University and its College of Engineering are grateful also to the members of its faculty who served on the Faculty Planning Committee for this conference. They were Rev. Virgil C. Blum, S.J., Associate Professor of Political Science; John Bradish, Assistant Professor of Mechanical Engineering; Rev. L. W. Friedrich, S.J., Chairman of the Department of Physics and Assistant Professor of Physics; James D. Graham, Assistant Professor of Electrical Engineering; Victor M. Hamm, Professor of English; James D. Horgan, Chairman of the Department of Electrical Engineering and Professor of Electrical Engineering; Robert A. Kidera, Professor of Journalism; Raymond J. Kipp, Assistant Professor of Civil Engineering; Dr. Ross C. Kory, Associate Professor of Medicine; Charles J. O'Neil, Professor of Philosophy; William B. Ready, Director of the Marquette University Libraries; John O. Riedl, Dean of the Graduate School; John W. Saunders, Jr., Chairman of the Department of Biology and Professor of Biology; and Dr. James J. Smith, Chairman of the Department of Physiology and Professor of Physiology.

Dr. Edward Teller

WHAT IS SCIENTIFIC EDUCATION?
THE PROBLEM TODAY

I SHOULD like to talk to you about a subject which I believe has a very great importance. At the end of the war there was no question where the leadership in science was to be found. It was to be found right here in this country. We had the best scientists, the biggest and best-trained group of engineers, the most forward-looking group of men in the applications of science to increase our power over nature and to use this power to the happiness and advancement of all.

If you would then have enumerated the other countries in the world, Russia would have come way down on the list. By quite a few of us, Russia might have been forgotten.

Today there is a question where the leadership lies. And there is no question which country is developing scientists most effectively. This

Edward Teller is professor of physics at the University of California; he is Director of the Radiation Laboratory at Livermore and Associate Director of the Radiation Laboratory at Berkeley.

Dr. Edward Teller

2 *What Is Scientific Education? The Problem Today*

country is Russia. I think there cannot be a shadow of a doubt that ten years from now, Russia will be the unquestioned leader in the scientific field.

This is something which I believe we cannot change, no matter what we do today. To educate a scientist is a long drawn-out process. It takes many years. The best minds are the youngest minds. The chief contribution to scientific work is made by people between, let us say, 25 and 30 years of age. The people on whom this duty will fall in ten years are learning today. They are in greater number and they are better educated in the Soviet Union than they are anywhere else. And even if we bend all our efforts to a change of the present situation, all we can hope for it to regain lost leadership later. That we are going to lose our leadership is inevitable.

Before I go on with this discussion, before I try to trace the reasons for this situation and before I venture to make suggestions how to improve our position, I should make clear to you one or two thoughts.

One thought is this. That advancement of science and advancement in education should be and is for me something admirable, no matter where and how it occurs. To my mind, the Russians are to be congratulated on their achievements, and to my knowledge in the whole story that unfolds behind the Iron Curtain, this is probably the only one in which we can and should take genuine pleasure.

On the other hand, I have another thought. And it is this. Science today is technology tomorrow. And technology means a better and more abundant life. Technology means a better state of defense and of military power. The Russians—we are all aware of this fact—are bent on world domination. If the present course is not changed, there is no doubt in my mind that the world before the end of this century will be modeled after Russian ideas and not after ideals of our own. This, I think, should leave you with no question about the importance I attribute to this particular issue. And it is with this in mind that I should begin to discuss with you the details.

First of all, how did Russia achieve this progress, this leadership or future leadership in science? Russia, by the organization of its country

Dr. Edward Teller

What Is Scientific Education? The Problem Today | 3

—an organization which does not simply find its roots in Communism but which goes back throughout the centuries—is the country where the individual is told what to do and he does it. After the Revolution the Russians were told, "We have to do something about science." A few months after the Revolution in Russia, the Commissar for Education, Lunacharsky, issued an order abolishing three letters in the Russian alphabet. These three letters were superfluous. Before that time, Russian spelling was almost, but not quite, phonetic. There were three sounds which could be written in one of two alternative ways. The three unnecessary letters were abolished. And Russian became a completely phonetic language.

Compare the Russian youngster with our luckless kids who learn in their first two years in school, by the example of reading and writing, that education is arbitrary, difficult and boring. They carry along this memory. Yet it is something about which it is immensely difficult for us to do anything and I don't propose that we do anything.

The Russians did other things, which I do not want to enumerate in detail. But they did one thing in particular. In Russia, a scientist is a privileged individual. He has all the honor, the comforts, and he has security also. This in Russia means more than it means in our country. We believe, and I think we believe rightly, that all of us should be respected if not honored; that all of us should have a comfortable life, and most of all, the life and liberty of all of us should be secure. This is as it should be. But in the Soviet Union a child knows that he can be comfortable only if he is a politician (a successful politician, that is) or a scientist. And he can be secure only if he is a scientist.

In order to embark on their scientific career, they work hard. They have to work hard. There is the whip of necessity which falls on every person in the Russian society.

I haven't visited the Soviet Union myself. But I have talked with many of my good scientific friends who have visited there. What they report is generally a friendly reception. The vituperations of the Soviet officials do not represent the feelings of the man on the street in Moscow. But when any one of my friends happened to have occasion to mention

DR. EDWARD TELLER

4 | *What Is Scientific Education? The Problem Today*

that he was a scientist, this was another thing again. He became a wonderful person, no matter where he came from. A scientist! This is really fine.

Now let us consider the position of the scientist in our country. Let me start by saying that I am going to criticize—but I am going to criticize in a matter which is not easily changed, and I can offer no easy remedies. The poor situation in science stems from a generally good situation of society as a whole; I will try to explain how in my mind these two things are connected. And I certainly don't want to change the general good background to save a detail even if that detail be ever so important. We shall have to think our way around this problem.

But first, let me try my hand at the diagnosis. I told you that the Russian children are driven on by the whip. Ours are not. And I think this is right. If we should embark on a competition in wielding a whip, there is no doubt that the Russians will win. Furthermore, the greatest accomplishments in this world are not accomplished by the whip. They are accomplished for other reasons—for reasons of inner necessity—and that is how it should be.

But this inner necessity is not independent of the circle in which we live. Man is a social animal. And the most social of the social animals is the child. He feels his way in a society new to him and he adapts himself to what is around him. And what does he see?

We live in a democracy. I am almost tempted to say that we live here, in this country, in the only true democracy the world has ever known. And by that I mean not only political democracy, not only that we have the means by which to determine our political fate. I mean more. Much more.

I mean economic democracy. I mean that all our production is for the masses. All value judgments are for the masses. What is good for just a few is not appreciated. What is good for everyone is paramount. This makes it more difficult for the privileged ones among us; because even if you have money, and even if you have not paid it all in taxes, you do not really have anything to spend it on. Because if you try to buy something that is better, you usually wind up with something that is merely different. That is, in my opinion, again as it should be. It takes the edge off of the competition that otherwise would be nasty. It takes away another motivation which is an external and really not thoroughly correct motivation, and throws the individual back into the freedom of his own soul where he can do with his otherwise comfortable life what he chooses. This is good, if applied to good people who know how to use their freedom.

But now let us consider the consequences of applying this thoroughly democratic order of things to the pursuit of intellectual achievements. Intellectual achievements are not attractive in themselves. The enjoyment of intellectual achievements is most definitely an acquired taste. You don't start out by liking classical music. You learn to like it. You don't start out by seeing the difference between good and bad architecture. You have to learn to see. And you sit down in front of a scientific treatise, and unless you have worked on it a lot, it might as well be Chinese.

Intellectual achievement is not, and perhaps never can be, for everybody. This is not appreciated in our democratic society. Now it has been said recently about the American public, about American opinion, that it is anti-intellectual. I believe that this is not so. American opinion is not anti-intellectual. It is *an*-intellectual. An intellectual is not resented; he is recognized as a person outside the common society. If he gets something accomplished, he is even greatly honored. He may be put on a pedestal, which is not the right place for him to be, in my opinion. But he is never, never understood.

When he begins to talk about his specialty to any but his closest colleagues he can, if he wishes to watch, notice the ear flaps coming down. Society says to the intellectual, says specifically to the scientist: "Go ahead and play, but leave us alone." Now this attitude by the public has produced a response from the scientists, and a response from the intellectuals. And this response is no less disastrous than the cause that has produced it. The response is this: "I am an intellectual. I love my subject. It is the whole world to me. Practically nothing else exists for me. And you people don't give a hang what I am doing. Well,

Dr. Edward Teller

6 | *What Is Scientific Education? The Problem Today*

I don't give a hang what you are doing. I will be by myself, go off into a corner with some of my close associates, and we'll talk to each other in polysyllables which only we understand, and sometimes I wonder whether anybody else understands me but myself."

There is a chasm separating the scientist from the common crowd. This chasm has been established on both sides, and both sides must make an effort to overcome it. Our society will not be healthy until, and unless, this chasm is bridged.

This chasm exists in science. It exists in education. You may recognize that science is important for our future, and you may tell your son, "Study mathematics, study physics. Those are the fields in which the future lies." And your son will evaluate your advice consciously and even more frequently but more effectively, non-consciously, in the light of what he sees you are doing. If you yourself know nothing about mathematics and know nothing about physics, why should he be different? When all the other children around him consider these subjects slightly ridiculous, why should he be different from them?

Let me dwell a little longer on the public attitude and on the attitude in the schools. Let me tell you right here and now the direction in which I wish we would be going. I think we should recognize, all of us, that in this technological age a person cannot be an educated person if he does not understand as much of the world that God has created as one can understand in general terms. And if we do not understand the changes that we men have made in this world around us, by the remarkable achievements of technology, we are not going to guide our future in the right way. As long as we consider the scientist as a magician, most often as a student of black magic we shall be ignorant strangers in this technological world.

Now let me give you a few examples. How many of you know how big an atom is? I would somehow imagine that this is an interesting piece of information. How many of you know the elementary principles according to which a modern computer can not only solve the most intricate mathematical problems but can translate idiomatically

DR. EDWARD TELLER

What Is Scientific Education? The Problem Today | **7**

one language into another? And by which it haltingly but effectively begins to learn how to play chess? How many of you know it?

I do not merely mean the electronics of a computer; I also mean its logical operation: the fact that there is no mental function which you can clearly define and which we cannot implant in that machine. How many of you know this?

Let me give you an example of another kind. During the last presidential election some of you might remember that there was a big discussion of a strange and not yet forgotten phenomenon called fallout. I am not going to tell you whether I am "for it or against it." But I will tell you about one of the few television shows that I have seen. And in that television show, there was a man, a good politcian, running for office. He would not say anything that isn't popular. He was asked about this question of fallout, and I forget whether he was for it or against it. But he said, "Now you know, I know nothing about nuclear physics, but . . ." And then he gave his opinion.

Assume that he had been asked a musical question. Would he have started his answer by, "Now you know, I never listen to the music of Beethoven, but. . . ." He would have known that with some of the voters, and not such a small number, this would have been unpopular. And even if it had been true, as a good politician he wouldn't have said it.

With nuclear science, it is otherwise. There, ignorance is today a political virtue.

This is the world in which our children make up their minds whether to become scientists or not. What professions do you think these children, the most alert of them, will choose? I know of one they are not likely to choose.

Now, as to the teaching of science. I would like to say a word about that, too.

I am sorry to confess to rather common taste in my reading, but I have to tell you that I like to read detective stories. These sentences in a very successful story struck me, and I quote:

"The rest of Thursday morning slipped by on leaden wings. I had dire trouble remaining awake (that is in a courtroom). A whole

Dr. Edward Teller

8 | *What Is Scientific Education? The Problem Today*

stream of alert, good-looking state police troopers paraded to the stand and like eager young professors in math talked endlessly and accurately about the charts of measurements."

The writer of this book is a very prominent legal authority. He is obviously a highly literate and cultured man. That is what he has to say, I am afraid not incorrectly, about a good math professor: he talks endlessly and accurately. He does.

When I look into my son's math assignments, I find questions like: "Farmer Jones owns 27 acres. On each square foot he grows a certain amount of wheat. He does this, having taken a loan at such and such percent interest." And then it goes on until finally my son has to calculate when the farmer will go broke. One such example would be fine, but there are dozens and dozens and dozens. And if he ever finishes with them, he might in the end qualify for the job of an accountant, but not for the job of a scientist.

Let me make a comparison. Not all of us are, and I think not all of us should be, musicians. But we try to educate our children in music and that is again as it should be. How do we do that? Do we select the easiest instrument—let us say, the piano, make sure that the child begins to learn the simplest thing on the piano, and tell him that for the next three years he must practice scales? What kind of outlook this will produce on music is easily imagined. This is in essence what we are doing in math and in some branches of science.

In music we teach our children music appreciation. In science we should teach everyone science appreciation—a knowledge of how far our scientific horizon extends. What are the simplest and most interesting facts in science? What are the surprises and unexpected things in science? These things everyone can understand. And when a person gets interested in these things, and when he catches a glimpse into the spirit of science, then he will have an entirely different outlook.

You have heard it said here before I started to talk, that scientists are involved in making decisions which affect the whole nation and, in fact, all of mankind. I should like to say that generally this is not so and should not be so. These important decisions belong to the people and to the representatives of the people who aren't and who shouldn't be, as a general rule, scientists. They make these decisions in a scientific world and, more frequently than not, they make them wrongly. I am advocating that they should be replaced in the next generation by people who have an ear for science as some people have an ear for music. They should be able to tell good science from poor by listening to the inner consistency, by understanding the connection in which statements occur. This is the art of government—a difficult art in every time and an impossibility if the mere elements of knowledge are lacking as they are in the scientific field. Also I am asking for an atmosphere in which a scientist will not be admired, not be put on a pedestal, but appreciated according to his merits and above all, understood. In this atmosphere, the small minority of our children who are really interested in science will become scientists, and this is the first decisive step in our educational problem.

So far I have talked at length about the diagnosis and I did so because I had a little confidence that in the main I am not wrong. Now I should like to talk about the cure; and this is infinitely more difficult. I will try to make suggestions only in order to be contradicted, because I do not imagine that my suggestions are right. At least they may get a discussion going.

First of all, how do we seek out the good material—the really talented scientists—among our children? I would like to tell you two things about them.

First of all, a good scientist starts young. My memory of my interest in numbers is older than any other memory I have. We cannot begin soon enough with the little games, the puzzles, with which a scientific education starts. And how do we recognize scientific talent? I would like almost to ask, What is scientific talent? To my mind, scientific talent is nothing more nor less than a strong, abiding interest in questions connected with science. This interest feeds on itself. The further you go, the more amusement you can have; science is an endless game with surprises around every corner. It is not different from a puzzle, only that it is more—it is a pyramid of puzzles that culminates

DR. EDWARD TELLER

10 | *What Is Scientific Education? The Problem Today*

in the kind of thing that nobody has ever dreamed about. It is this interest in puzzles, it is this tenacity—the losing sight of everything else while one is immersed in this particular activity—which you can notice in some children and which should be and can be encouraged from the very beginning.

We have grave problems. The gravest problem that faces us now is that we do not have enough teachers and we do not have good teachers in science. Let me tell you what I think a good teacher should be. You have heard frequently that a good teacher is a person who knows how to teach. In fact, the education of our teachers is based on this obvious doctrine. I think this doctrine is erroneous. Many obvious things are erroneous. I also have heard a different statement, that a good teacher is someone who knows his subject. Well, to know one's subject is an advantage, but I do not think that this is so terribly important either. The most important thing in a good teacher is that he should love his subject, and that the love of his subject should be plainly visible to his pupils.

I have been told that we are all descendants of monkeys, and this fact is most evident in our children. And like good monkeys that they are, if I get up in front of them and talk about something which I clearly enjoy, they will want to imitate me, and they will find a way to enjoy it too. If I make a mistake because I don't know my subject well enough, that only adds to the fun, as long as I don't insist on my mistakes and as long as I demonstrate to them that the most common situation in which a scientist finds himself is to make mistakes, recognize them, and correct them. Such teachers we do not have today. The general direction in which I would like to change the education of our teachers is obvious. But this is a slow process, and I would like to recommend to you a number of things we could do right away.

One of them is this: in our public schools no one is allowed to teach except somebody who has gotten the official stamp of approval by having learned in a laborious manner not what to teach, but how to teach. We are, as far as science is concerned, in a real emergency. Our future, our freedom, is at stake. I think that it is necessary, as an emergency measure, that we permit anyone with an an appropriate degree to teach in our schools—let us say master's or doctor's degree—in mathematics, in science, physics or chemistry, or in engineering. I believe that many of our university professors will be willing to give of their time in individual lectures or even in a regular course at our high schools.

I know that many of our industries will allow some of their scientific employees to take time off, without loss of pay, and tell school children about the excellent work that is going on in industry and to make them better acquainted with the workings of our technology.

These are simple and practical steps. The schools would not have to ask for the services of a man who does not have the knack of teaching. They could select the right teachers—the best teachers. And I think it would be a great stimulus.

Among our regular teachers we should give the highest reward to those who teach successfully and who keep teaching successfully. I would suggest—just as an idea—that there be established an honor society of teachers—I mean elementary and high school teachers. The members of that society would not have any additional duties but they would have the distinguished privilege of obtaining an additional salary equal to the salary they are making as teachers—a salary which would expire together with their membership in the honor society as soon as they take a job other than teaching.

The question is how to select these really successful teachers. I would not select them by examining them. I would select them by looking at the children whom they taught. If really successful boys and girls come from their schools into the colleges and universities, if their pupils gain honors in considerable numbers in science fairs; if they do well in the scholarship examinations; then those teachers who have produced these good scientific minds must be good teachers. And what is the secret of a good teacher? I do not know. But I would like to measure the quality of the teaching by its success.

Another suggestion: I think that we should make more use of counsellors. We have, in our high schools, counsellors who give their

DR. EDWARD TELLER

12 | *What Is Scientific Education? The Problem Today*

counsel to the teachers. We need traveling counsellors, particularly in the rural districts, who give their advice to the students, who go two or three times each year to the schools, talk with the talented students, inspire them, give them books to read, keep an eye on them. By relatively little contact, a lot can be accomplished.

When my father, who was a lawyer, discovered that I had some real interest in playing with numbers, he went to an old friend, a university professor in Projective Geometry—not considered generally a very inspiring subject. This Professor Klug had a few conversations with me—not many. I was then 10 years of age. He determined my future. Because no matter what the subject was, it was something into which I could dig my teeth, and there was the obvious fact that Professor Klug had more fun than any grownup I had met to that date.

I think that contact with practicing scientists, whether as teachers or counsellors, would do a lot for our youngsters.

There is still another approach and perhaps the most fruitful one. I mean the use of television and films. How to do it I do not know. There are probably as many approaches as there are people—I tried it myself. I think that if many of us scientists tried to express ourselves clearly, we could get these adventurous and inspiring ideas into every home and into the mind of every child.

I would like to make another suggestion. My enjoyment of the frequent phenomenon of commercial advertising is rather on the moderate side. This advertising does not usually give me a great surprise except the surprise of feeling that this particular product too is stupendous and better than anything else. I somehow have the feeling that most people must be tired of being talked down to in such an idiotic manner. I wonder what would happen if some of our big companies, who can afford it, would in lieu of advertisement give a five or ten minute talk by one of their practicing scientists on one of the problems in which he is interested. He could say what the oil production people are thinking about the methods of drilling holes in the ground or where to dig them. He could talk about the marvelous structures which act as molecular filters, letting through only molecules of a certain size.

A simple, single idea can be transmitted inside of ten minutes in such a way that every alert youngster will be able to pick it up. This will be indirect, but effective advertising, and not only directed to the future customer, but also, what is equally important, to the future employee.

I wonder how many of these ideas and what other ideas we could use. One advantage we have over the Russians is that each of us can think independently; and each of us can carry his ideas to the free market where it will be adopted or rejected, not always according to its merits, but frequently according to its merits.

I have talked to you longer than what I consider is the proper length of a lecture. I will, however, ask you to listen to me even longer on a subject on which I am rabid. And this subject is the metric system of measurement. In 1927, the Russians did away with whatever versts and other absurd units they had and like most of the rest of the world, they completely adopted the metric system. Also relatively recently, the Hindus and the Japanese have adopted it.

But there are still some wild Anglo-Saxon tribes which cherish their traditions above everything else. Let me mention to you a few of these traditions. It is said that King Henry I established the yard by measuring the distance between the tip of his finger and the tip of his nose. It is indubitably true because it is found in the 17th pronouncement of King Edward II that an inch is three, dry, round barley corns laid end to end. You all know that the mile comes from the Latin "mille" or thousand, for the thousand double steps of the average Roman soldier. The French, who since that time have improved their ways, had a more civilian and more civil measure of great length; and that was the "pipe"—the distance you can walk while smoking your pipe.

The scientists believe in a strange thing, the CGS system, in which seemingly quite unrelated things like magnetism, time, space, and weight are all related to each other. The English system is much more diversified. There length and area are measured in quite independent units, in feet and in acres. Volume is something different again. In our country it is measured by the old Queen Anne's wine gallon. Incidentally, in the mother country this has been superseded by the

Imperial wine gallon which is kept in the Tower of London and which is obviously more practical because it contains almost a quart more of liquid.

I would like to tell you one more story about lengths. Right now the inch is undergoing one of those great reforms. It used to be defined by the National Bureau of Standards as 2.540005 centimeters. This is the American inch. The Australian inch is 2.54-nothing centimeters. And the British inch, with appropriate understatement, is 2.53999-something centimeters. There have been attempts to agree and we have agreed with the Australians on 2.540, which the British are right now taking under favorable consideration. In the meantime, the revolution has broken out among the geodetists in this country. All our coast and geodetic survey maps are based on 2.540005 centimeters and so our miles would be off by many thousands of an inch. The revolution was successful and now this country has two inches—the international inch and the geodetic inch.

You may know that our temperature scale comes from an erudite German, Gabriel Daniel Fahrenheit. Mr. Fahrenheit waited in Danzig until it had got as cold as it could get. Then on the day that was absolutely the coldest possible, he stuck his thermometer out the window, and that was zero. Then he put it under his arm. He seemed to have a slightly elevated temperature, and that became 100. So the history of our system of temperatures goes back to the fact that there was once, in a rather cold town, a rather hot guy.

The scientific system of measurement which has been invented in the French Revolution is considerably more prosaic. It has less to do with barley corns and arms' lengths and things like that, and a little more to do with the measurement of the earth, which in a millenium or two will again look provincial but right now it is what we share with all humanity.

This method of measurements is based on the decimal system and is therefore a great time-saver. If we would introduce this system, we would reap immediate and great benefits: simpler work in engineering, and an end to the schizophrenia which now exists between

Dr. Edward Teller

What Is Scientific Education? The Problem Today | **15**

engineering on the one hand and science on the other hand. Whenever these two meet, they have first to explain their terms, have to translate laboriously from inches to centimeters and vice-versa.

If we do not introduce this metric system our children will continue to sweat over questions such as: How many grains are there in a gram? How many liters make up an acre foot? Before they can dig their teeth into any real problem of science, before they can catch a glimpse of the order, the scope and the beauty of the universe they are stultified by the man-made confusion and boredom of the arithmetic of the inches.

It is time for a change. If we do not change, we shall lose in the economic competition with Russia. If a man has a chance of buying a piece of machinery in which he understands how to replace a screw and how to measure that screw without the introduction of a whole new branch of learning, he will buy that simple machinery. So far the English-speaking world has enjoyed a practical monopoly. This is at an end. We are faced by a powerful competitor who is going to come into his own in the next decade. And we have to prepare for that competition as well as for the competition in the scientific and military fields.

Our present Secretary of Commerce has laid plans to go over in a considered and careful manner the metric system of measurements. He has asked the Bureau of Standards to work out the means by which the transition can be performed gradually and as painlessly as possible, but also as speedily as possible. We have untold millions of dollars invested in the screws and nuts and bolts and other units which go into our industrial machinery. All this will not be changed easily. It will not be changed without resistance, but changed it must be if we are to educate our children in an expeditious manner and if we are to live with our neighbors successfully.

I have told you everything that I can reasonably tell you about scientific education and some other thing as well. Let me take a very short time to talk to you about an even more general subject of which education is but a little part.

I have started out by telling you that we must respect and take

Dr. Edward Teller

16 | *What Is Scientific Education? The Problem Today*

pleasure in the accomplishments, in the scientific progress that has taken place behind the Iron Curtain. There can be no greater mistake than to underestimate the Russians and the Communist empire. To my mind, together with this appreciation which may be the basis of a future understanding, there must go another realization. Russia, the Communist world, is a machine. It is a magnificent machine. It is an admirable machine. But it is a machine. And the men in Russia are no more than parts of this machine. We in the free world have the enjoyment and responsibility of being free, of not being told what we should do and should not do. This can be a curse and it can be a blessing. If we take a shallow view of our responsibility, it is a curse. And this curse has been demonstrated in many of the mistakes of which we all have been, and are, guilty.

It can be a blessing, because the highest achievements come through the inner conviction, through the inventiveness, through the ideas, through the dedication that I cannot imagine to be associated with anything but freedom. We, the free people of the free world, are faced with a great challenge. In mere size, in geographic space, and numbers of people involved, in the concreteness and the suddenness of the dangers that face us, it is a greater challenge than ever has faced humanity. I won't say that it is the greatest challenge in every respect, because each age feels its own challenge as the most unique and the most terrible thing that could be. It is our challenge; it is our world.

I feel that the basic fact of this challenge is this: the world has become very small. We do influence our neighbors. Our neighbors do influence us. Today we have learned how to harness the atom. Tomorrow we are likely to find out how to influence the weather. Man has cultivated the land for millenia. We may soon find out how to cultivate the oceans.

All this is impossible for an individual, for a company, even for a nation. It cannot be accomplished except by a cooperation between nations. The question before us is this: Shall that cooperation be enforced by an iron rule or shall it be a cooperation between free partners? We know our answer. We know the difficulties of the adjustments that

Dr. Edward Teller

What Is Scientific Education? The Problem Today | **17**

go with our answer, and we would like to take time to work out our solution. But time is what we don't have, because the Russians on the other side are not taking time.

There is going on today, in the world, a revolution of the under-dog of yesterday. It is the revolution which has been called the revolution of rising expectations. It proceeds along with the turbulent expansion of the industrial revolution over the whole world. Who will lead that revolution? We, or they? The advantages of direct action, of strict organization, is with them. We have nothing but the ability of the individual. It rests on the individual, on each of us, whether this revolution will bring about a world which will be slave, or a world that will be free. And the education of the scientist is an integral and an important part of that fateful decision.

Rev. Gustave Weigel, S.J.

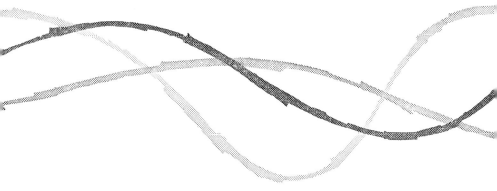

WHAT DOES RELIGION DEMAND
OF THE SCIENTIFICALLY EDUCATED?

THE question proposed for consideration at this point is what does religion demand of the man scientifically trained. A quick answer is possible. It demands of the scientist just what it demands of anybody else: all of him.

This quick answer is true but it requires a good deal of reflection to discover the relevant content of this truth. Religion is not only an idea; it is also an image. As an idea it has no foes, especially if we understand the idea as a life of devotion to the ultimate, be that conceived as a personal agent or as an impersonal binding force of the universe. The image, on the other hand, is not so appealing. It says for many, fanaticism, superstition, hypocrisy and stubborn ignorance. Re-

Rev. Gustave Weigel, S.J., is professor of ecclesiology
at Woodstock (Md.) College.

ligion as an image makes many a thoughtful man shrink from it even though he is attracted by the idea.

Besides this general ambiguity of religion in our society, the realm of science offers an added problem. By this time we know that science as such does not render the scientist a foe of religion. Too many scientists have been deeply religious. We need think only of men like Robert Boyle and his contemporary, Isaac Newton, who were not only landmarks in the evolution of modern science but they also fancied themselves as theologians. Einstein was devoted to divinity which he conceived to be the mysterious matrix of all reality, though this is not the conception of his own Jewish tradition. Names like these could be multiplied endlessly. Yet it must be recognized that the man of science, pure or applied, is often even contemptuous of religion as he finds it in his existential community. When this occurs, we note that the scientist does not deal with the religious question by means of rational analysis. He just refuses to deal with it at all.

We can see the reasons for such a reaction. Science by its method is empirical. In matters abstract it uses mathematics which can be highly abstruse and subtle. However, mathematics is a formal science. It makes no affirmations about the order of human concern. It is indifferent to the use made of its findings and the findings themselves have an utter purity which cannot be related to the problem of the significance of man or of God's ways with men. Any man trained in the disciplines of science by necessity deals with the palpable world which he organizes with the aid of neutral mathematics. Such a training neither affirms nor denies divinity. It laudably abstracts from it.

That the scientist is a man with his own anxieties is a truth recognized by all. Yet how he solves the aporiae engendered by existence cannot be a formal preoccupation of the school of science, for it has no means in its proper panoply to cope with such questions. For many a student of science the abstraction from all which is meta-empirical, a tactic proper to his school, becomes a principle of life. It is not that he has given the matter of religion much thought, but unfortunately when he does think, he can only do so in accord with the methods he learned in his scientific training. He cannot adequately handle the religious problem, or at best he is gauche at it. It is not surprising, then, that he steers away from it. The result can easily be a coldness to the religious or a superficiality in his practice of religion.

I have tried honestly to depict the situation of religion in a school of science. The situation indicates the existence of a problem. The problem is how the school of science can deal with the religious question. Answers have already been given. In Marxist countries science is used to kill religion. Actually a paradox is involved here. There is no more religious man in the world than a convinced Marxist. He is fighting not against religion but for it, but the religion he wants is energetically hostile to all religions but his own. The Marxist is a man of intense faith but he has called this faith science. There is a Marxist God who, or better, which, is the basic determining force of the universe. It is eternal and the creator of all things. It has revealed itself in history and we can know it. It has its prophets in Marx, Engels and Lenin. There are sacred books. There is a vivid cult in parades, ritual, icons and prayer-like slogans. There is a deep mystique in the whole movement—and like all young religions it is highly fanatical.

Hence the Marxist solution to the question of religion in scientific training is not what it pretends to be. It is actually the one solution which consciously uses science to teach a specific religion. This was clearest in the case of the Russian biologist Lysenko who derived his conclusions not so much from observable data but from religious dogma. Other men of science were skeptical but the Marxist hierarchy gave him its blessing and with it he could thrive.

To anyone who has even a slight knowledge of the meaning of the scientific enterprise the Russian theory of the relationship between science and religion is disagreeable. It is wise for us to see that this reaction would be just as strong if some religion other than Marxism were to consider scientific training in the same way. It was not hostility to religion which made and still makes many scientists suspicious of science institutes under the control of religious bodies. They fear the intrusion of non-scientific imperatives into scientific thought. Actually in the Western world of our time the scientific schools under religious auspices bend over backwards to avoid the accusation that their rationale and method are not rigorously scientific. The scientific disciplines are not tampered with because of religious faith and as a rule the scientific schools of a religious center of studies have little or no clerical control in matters academic. The clergy themselves urge the faculties of their scientific departments to proceed without fear or preoccupation because of theological orthodoxies. This general attitude is healthy and confirms the views of men at large that scientific training must not be hampered by concerns derived from religious faith.

In the light of these observations I think that it is safe to say that we do not want schools of science either to champion religion or to fight it. We feel that somehow this is not the function of an engineering school.

Is it then necessary to consider the school of pure or applied science as religiously neutral? Must the future scientist be trained in an environment sealed off from religion, so aloof that religion simply is out of place in the school? This hardly seems to be the answer, because as we have seen, such chilling neutrality makes it difficult for good minds scientifically trained to consider the religious question adequately.

At this point it seems that we have reached a total impasse. We want a science school which will not concern itself with religion and at the same time lend itself to aid its students to meet the religious issue responsibly.

I think that the contradiction will evaporate if we consider all the dimensions of scientific training. Everywhere in the United States professors in schools of engineering or in centers of scientific preparation lament the rawness of their students in branches other than those directly pertinent to their scientific instruction. We are told that they cannot spell and that they do not read books. The great cultural heritage of our human family is unknown to them. The cry is everywhere that the training in the past has been too narrow and the product a bit of a barbarian.

It is not for me to say that the accusation is valid. But the accusation does point to something that either is or should be in engineering and science institutes. This is a department of humanistic studies. No one wants a science school to turn out poets or philosophers, but the possibility of such a product should not be ruled out. If all we feed the candidates for a science degree is science exclusively, we shall not get good scientists. A scientist is a human being before he is a scientist and he should develop his humanity no less than his scientific bents. The good scientist should be rich in imagination because it plays a part in scientific creativity. A scientist should know history because it will reveal to him what has been done and what has been found to be fruitless. No school of science wishes to turn out mere electrical brains because we must have someone to feed these mechanisms with ideas which can then be mathematically organized by the machine. Such devices are not creative tools; they are only logical aids. The day when our scientists know only science we are lost because they will not be able to solve problems of man; only problems of a non-human mental field. The great scientist must be a man of vision and insight, and these two indispensable qualities cannot be conveyed by engineering schools nor can they be developed if the school communicates exclusively scientific lore. Philosophy is necessary, even if it is only presented as history. For the scientist who knows what he is doing the philosophy of science and its relation to a total philosophy are of prime import.

Courses of language, history and philosophy belong to the engineering school, not because they are a part of engineering but because they are needed by a man who is an engineer. Of course we run into a difficulty here which must be well known to the directors of scientific institutes. They probably see clearly the importance of humanistic studies in their schools but because of an inertia which affects students of all kinds, the students themselves with a false pragmatism refuse the humanities on the ground that they are not relevant to engineering. If the humanistic branches are made compulsory, the students sabotage the endeavor by doing skimpy work in these branches.

One solution for this grave problem will be a greater concern for the humanities professors than with the teachers of science. There must be something prophetic and stimulating about the instructor of humanities in science schools. He must attract the students in spite of their allergy to the message he has to give. Perhaps by paying better salaries and giving signs of high esteem to the professors of the humanities the scientific institutes will be able to draw on the best men in the field, which certainly is not true today if we look at our engineering schools by and large.

It is in the humanistic department of the science school curriculum where religion will have its proper and necessary place. Theology is not only a discipline necessary for the clergyman but it is the capstone of a humanistic training. No philosophy and no literature and no history can avoid the religious question. The mature man must face the religious challenge and come to some kind of stand on this matter because it deals with the ultimate concern of man. If our budding scientist has never even seen the problem or has refused to deal with it seriously when seen, he is only an adolescent no matter how bright or old he is. The divine is as much a field of reality as is the resistance of materials. It is humanly speaking more important, even though not as urgent, than other questions because it involves man's overall concern which works itself out in every concern.

No one would expect theological questions studied in the engineering school to have the form and depth assumed in the school of religion. But enough should be given in intellectual terms to bring the problem clearly to focus so that the student will be forced to give some kind of answer which will structure his life both for the moment and for later days. What is more, every facility should be given by the school so that deeper questions, should they arise, be ventilated at least in private conference with someone prepared in the field.

So far I have insisted on the intellectual dimension of religion. It is under this aspect that religion has a legitimate and necessary place in scientific training. Yet religion is more than an intellectual effort. It demands of its adepts a full response, not merely the response of reason. The expositors of religious thought should bring this out in their lectures. There is a laboratory side to the theory of religion. It is hardly enough to know the speculative nucleus of charity. Until it is practiced, it will never be understood truly. St. Augustine in one place asks what is love. He answers: give me a lover and he will know what it is. The man who has never loved will never understand it at all. The religious program of the engineering school must in consequence have some kind of plan of religious action under the direction of the teachers of religion.

So far we have dealt abstractly with the problem of scientific training and religion. We must in candor deal with the practical side of the problem. The student of science if he is worth his salt must be immersed in his subject. It is well known that engineering students have a heavy curriculum where leisure, if not totally absent, at least is much scarcer than in the schools of the arts. Likewise the type of thinking in science courses is diffrent from that employed in the humanities. It is hard therefore for the student to turn off his main current of thought to follow a direction requiring a totally different use of intelligence.

Then, too, the young scientist wants to be a scientist. That is why he is in this department of the university rather than in another. A certain exclusiveness of interest will affect all of his existence and it will produce discomfort and even guilt feelings if he gives time and effort to studies which are not immediately relevant to his central anxiety. He can easily be tempted to reflect on the truth that after all a man who is religiously illiterate can still be a respectable scientist. Nor does such illiteracy imply any hostility to religious reality.

In other words we are faced practically with a strong resistance in the students in general to a serious and rational consideration of religion. It seems wiser to recognize this fact than to deny its existence.

One way of meeting this difficulty is by the use of law. By university rules the student will be forced to take part in the study of religion. It can be doubted if this is the solution to the problem. The old saw tells us that you can drive a horse to water but you cannot make him drink. In our difficulty it is of little comfort to know that we have brought the students to the fountain. We are anxious to have him drink, and we shall not accomplish this by law. He must be attracted by the vitality and brilliance of the courses.

Then too we must bear in mind the difference between importance and urgency. It is important to get to school in proper mental and physical conditions but it is definitely more urgent to get there in any form whatsoever. In human affairs importance cedes to urgency. The science student is urgently overwhelmed by a heavy load of scientific meditation. He just cannot take much time to devote it to matters which may well be more important. If the religion professors of the university make great demands on the engineer, he can only ignore them. Religious instruction is only one thin strand woven into a total cable and it cannot be the whole of the cable. However, it can by its color or texture be a conspicuous strand as indeed it should be. But on every count religious instruction must be minimal rather than maximal. The engineering school does not turn out theologians though it does wish to turn out cultured scholars.

One more conclusion we can draw from our consideration of the situation of the engineering students is that the classes which deal humanistically with religion—and it is not necessary that they be so titled—propose with clarity the theological dimension of reality and the importance of a proper answer to the religious question for the total well-being of the future scientist. Clarity and relevance should be the tone of religious instruction in the science school. The rationale and structure of theology in a school of divinity is out of place in the engineering college. Here religion is presented not so much as a discipline of its own but rather as a phase of disciplines related to scientific research. It does not mean that we make religion "practical" for the student. Rather it means that we stress its humanistic relevance.

There is one last question which we must face before we conclude. Is the religion of the scientist specifically distinct from that of the baker, the cobbler and the candle-stick maker? The question is more involved than it at first sight seems. It is true that every man's religiosity is uniquely his own so that in no two men shall we find the identical response to the same religious stimulus. Some men, unfortunately few, react powerfully to religious demands. Most react with lesser degrees of ardor. It is also true that the religion of the intellectual will take on an intellectualistic tinge. He may be far more interested in the confection of an intellectual scheme of religion than in being a vital participant in liturgy. It is certainly not something strange if an empirical scientist should show himself cool to the niceties of metaphysical formulas of religious endeavor. Yet religion is all of these things and more than all of them. There have been men in the history of our earth for whom the secular veils which hide the divine visage were thin, though they are thick enough for the vast majority of mortals. For men of clairvoyance it is not too hard to see God in the movement of the stars, in the splendor of a flower, in the mysterious harmonies of whirling atoms. It seems to me that mathematics, physics and astronomy can easily be a hot-bed for mysticism, though not for theology.

Yet such men are not made by the university nor can it unmake them. Congenital psychic structure makes such a man peculiarly sensitive to the order of the divine. Theologians would call it a grace— something freely given by a gracious God. But Blaise Pascal and Albert Einstein who were men like this, are not the common or garden variety of scientists. The majority of this brotherhood shows little mystical propensity. Ergs, ohms, foot-pounds, and volts are the measures they use for taping the universe. God is not too visible to them even if they are sincerely religious.

Religiosity has its modes. The Sister of Charity who nurses the sick will have quite a different view of religion than the contemplative Carmelite. The Carmelite by reason of her way of life will be afraid of the body. The Sister of Charity works with the human body all day long and has no fear of it. The human organism is no forbidden mystery to her and she takes it for granted without any emotional reaction at all. In her close contact with the sheerly physical side of man she evolves her own religious life. It will be a rare case when she sees God in the functions of the human liver. She will be prone to look at the liver in a way not unlike that whereby the garage mechanic considers a carburetor. The divine dimension of these things is hardly considered.

A superficial critic will call both the mechanic and the Sister of Charity materialists but this kind of criticism is so irrelevant. Matter is no less divine in its origins than spirit and God manifests Himself in both of them.

What is more, to work with matter is undoubtedly a creative action. The pure scientist constructs matter ideally and the applied scientist changes the hard matter at hand to make it serve the purposes of man. The first destiny given to man according to the words of Genesis was the task of subduing the earth and establishing dominion over it. The biblical descriptions are of the material earth and man must take matter seriously. He is an instrument of creation which was not a once-and-for-all action but the continuous act of God now involving human instrumentality. The bridge-builder cannot help but feel the thrill of creation when he sees the clean esthetic lines of his finished structure. He is a creator and in his creative action he works in God. The pure scientist when he has achieved his chaste equations must feel like God who understands perfectly the essence of matter. Such activities are highly religious if only the men involved in them would reflect deeply on what they have done.

As we have said, we must not expect all scientists to be mystically inclined. Yet even those far removed from mysticism still are engaged in divine-human creation. They are not far from God but very near Him. This nearness, unconscious though it be, sanctifies the man of science.

If then there is a specific religiosity for men of science, I would say that it would derive from the notion of creativity whereby the scientist shares in the action of God the creator. We know that the scientist will rarely reflect on this dimension of his work, but ontologically, in the objective order, his closeness to divinity is a fact.

It would seem, therefore, that religion should be presented in schools of science from the standpoint of creativity exercised on matter. Other aspects of religious life can well be skipped because either they will be unattractive or irrelevant. The scientist as this man, will have his unique structure and it may well be that because of structural propensities religion can be attractive from some other angle of approach. In this respect the scientist is no different from any other man. But as a scientist, and the schools of science look on their students mainly in this light, he will be near to God in his scientific creativity.

The creative aspect of divinity, the creative function of religion, a piety of creation seem to be good starting points for religious instruction in schools of science. But they will have to be supplemented with some consideration of religious epistemology, for in this field there can be real difficulty for someone working steadily by the empirical method.

When I speak of religious epistemology I mean a discussion of the levels of predication. A positivist is prone to demand that statements be formed in univocal predication. One word must mean one thing, and that thing can be described precisely with reference to empirical data. This kind of affirmation is rare in religious language by reason of the nature of the religious enterprise. The man accustomed to positivistic affirmations must be warned that deep religious truth by reason of its non-empirical nature needs other forms of expression.

Such other types of affirmation will be either mythical or symbolic. These two kinds of predication must be understood and distinguished. Mythical statement points to its object but it does not affirm it nor does it describe it. It evokes a conventional image by a literary form of speech which puts the reader or hearer in a mood wherein he can see beyond the image. When the poet spoke of the cruel, crawling foam he obviously was not talking of empirical foam which is neither cruel nor crawling. He was arousing a feeling of resentful sadness at the death of Mary in the sea. He wanted to point to an unmerited death and he did so mythically, through the use of images well known by his contemporaries. Thus the Hebrews spoke of the bowels of God's mercy and we speak of His tender heart. These are mythical expressions and have nothing to do with entrails or bodily organs; much less with contemporary theories about them.

Religion will use myth in its message because this kind of predication is rich in pointing value. If such assertions are understood literally, that is, in logical predication, they are only nonsense.

But the most important kind of religious communication is symbolic statement. A symbol is not a myth. It wishes to do more than evoke an image which can only serve as a pointer to something beyond itself. A symbol is an analogy where the analogy is intrinsic and ontological. It really and truly states something of its object but with an attribute which is linguistically proper to an entirely different object. When God is called the father of men we are saying something which is absolutely true of God but not in a way in which paternity is true of my human father. It is the symbolic statement which is all important in religion. It requires meditation to see its depth and content.

With an initial description of the modes of religious predication in contrast with logical affirmation, the young scientific student can begin to understand something of the religious side of life. Directing him along the lines of creation which is his own proper activity he can make religion meaningful to himself. It seems that through such a training we can have what we want: a scientist who is a strictly true scientist and at the same time a man for whom religion is real and significant.

Senator Paul H. Douglas

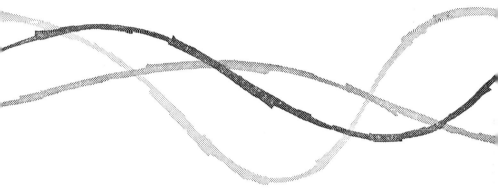

WHAT DOES FREE SOCIETY DEMAND
OF THE SCIENTIFICALLY EDUCATED?*

FIRST of all, let me say that a free society expects that its scientists and engineers will know their jobs. No amount of social consciousness can compensate for lack of expertness in the fundamental principles of mechanics, electricity, and chemistry, and in the ways in which the tremendous powers latent in nature can be most efficiently, economically, and safely employed.

Frequently, scientists and engineers, like other technicians—even in the social sciences—become impatient with the theoretical foundations of their sciences and become concerned only with their applied aspects. This is, of course, a mistake. I do not believe that a man can

* Author's revision of a speech delivered at Marquette University College of Engineering, May 21, 1959. Abstracted with permission of Senator Douglas and Marquette University.

Senator Paul H. Douglas is Democratic Senator from Illinois.

be a truly first-rate engineer, for example, unless he is also trained in theoretical physics and chemistry with ample laboratory work. He should recognize that success in these subjects increasingly rests on a thorough mastery of mathematics, a mastery which is equally basic in applied engineering.

I believe that one educational consequence of this is that we should offer, perhaps require, more mathematics in the high schools and teach it better. To help in this work, the better students should be put on a separate track where they can do more and better work; then mathematics and science can be made part of the core for all academically able students and particularly for those who are scientifically inclined.

I would suggest, moreover, that science is a cultural as well as a rational and applied subject. Its study gives one new respect for the intellectual powers of mankind, of how physical truth must be discovered and continually sought, and of how truth is not static but unfolding. Certainly the modern discoveries of the vastness of the universe on the one hand and the amazingly complex structures of atoms and chromosomes on the other should cure any tendency toward human cockiness and lead instead to that wonder which, as Plato said, is the beginning of all philosophy.

But the engineer or the scientist tends also to become a superintendent, a business manager, an industrial executive. It is not solely occupational bias, therefore, which makes me believe that an engineer should know economics. Everyone, to be sure, who earns or spends is an economist, whether conscious of that fact or not. The most effective use of time, resources, and money is the subject matter of economics and is, therefore, the stuff of which a large part of life is made. Here, then, is another field of study—economics—which might well be sharpened and strengthened for many or most students in the upper years of high school. And I have not the least doubt but that we need to do a far better job of this at the college level.

But thus far, I have been merely elaborating upon the need for scientific engineering, and economic competence. There is no substitute for this, but most certainly it is not all that a free society should expect. Society has the right to expect that its experts shall be concerned with the end effects of their work and, indeed, the purpose of life itself as well as mere technicalities.

Engineers have been subject to justified criticism in the past on the ground that they have been so absorbed in construction and operation that they have paid scant attention to the purposes for which their work was being used. Leonardo da Vinci served willingly as military adviser and engineer for Caesar Borgia. Moreover, as city planner in Milan for Lodovico Sforza, he drew plans for a future city where only the aristocracy were to be allowed to live in the sunlight, while the common people were to be compelled to live and work underground. In a similar fashion, the Great German engineers worked just as willingly for Hitler as they had for industry under the Weimar Republic. A lot of technical skill went into the construction of the gas chambers where six million Jews and anti-Nazis were gassed to death by Hitler.

We do not know a great deal about the Russian engineers under Communism. At times, they have been made the victims of false charges and brutal purges. But at times they seem in the main to have put their talents freely at the disposal of a merciless police state which in turn has developed and rewarded them as long as they did not question either its goals or its tactics.

Similarly, in this country we have seen talented engineers serving loyally and effectively under brutal managements without any apparent twinges of conscience. And engineers have commonly been all too ready to serve on almost any terms those who have held political and industrial power. Absorbed in the technical nature of their work, they have been relatively impervious to the purposes of that which they have operated. Yet they and we need to recognize that the sciences and engineering techniques are neither moral nor immoral as such but are rather amoral and can serve the degradation as well as the enhancement of life.

There is another factor which needs, I think, to be frankly

faced. That is the fact that if one becomes absorbed in the manipulation of material forces, there is a natural tendency to become somewhat unconcerned about their effect on human beings. Those who have watched the post-war spread of suburban subdivisions, or the urban sprawl, know how beautiful trees and rolling countrysides have been eliminated in order to produce a deadly uniformity which can only ultimately lead to further claustrophobia.

This whole problem is highlighted by the moral dilemma created by the development of the atomic and hydrogen bomb and the development of the intermediate and intercontinental missiles. Ever since the validity of Einstein's theorem that $E = mc^2$ was established, it was inevitable that sooner or later the enormous energies within the atom would be unleashed. It was a wise decision of President Roosevelt to try to develop the bomb for, had we not done so, there was every probability that the Nazis with their own scientists and engineers would. Then science would indeed have been used to enslave the world and to destroy freedom. And freedom is a deep reality and not merely a word.

The physicists who worked upon the bomb, a large proportion from my own university, performed wonders. We all know what followed. The atom bomb was succeeded by the hydrogen bomb and fusion has achieved infinitely greater destruction than fission. As was inevitable, knowledge spread. Today, three nations have the bomb. In a few years, a dozen promise to have it. The human race now has the power to blow itself off the face of the earth. In the meantime, if the testing continues in its present form for a considerable period and is joined in by additional nations—and I emphasize all these qualifications—we may expect a marked increase in leukemia and cancer of the bones from the fallout of strontium 90. In addition, the genetic effects upon future generations will probably be most damaging.

Now, I do not think anyone is really to blame for all this. It was indeed probably inevitable and one consequence has flowed naturally from another as did events in a Greek tragedy.

But I submit that scientists and engineers should not be indifferent to the possible terrible consequences of all this. They opened Pandora's box. They unleashed the forces within the atom. They gave men the power to achieve their own destruction. They cannot in full conscience walk away from what they have bequeathed to mankind and passively allow others to deal with the problem which they have created. We citizens need the trained and informed help of those who have let the genie out of the bottle.

Nor can scientists content themselves with the safeguard proposed by Francis Bacon over three centuries ago in his *New Atlantis.* For in that book which forecast the age of science, Bacon proposed a gigantic research institute called "Philosophers' House" and as his scientists let loose a new invention upon the earth, they fell upon their knees and prayed that it might be used for the benefit and not for the injury of mankind. But we cannot expect the Divine Power to do it all for us. We must do something for ourselves. That, I think, is what most of the great scientists such as Einstein, Urey, and others, who brought the atom bomb into being, strove for when, with help of a great Senator, Brian McMahon of Connecticut, they worked to have the development of atomic energy put under civilian rather than military control.

This was an important first step. But it was only a first step. The great issue remaining lies now in the field of international relations and the relations between the communist and free world. Here we need cool heads, brave hearts, and compassionate souls.

I am not one who blames the United States for the head-on collision which seems to be looming. The overwhelming proportion of the fault lies with the communist rulers of Russia. They are, I believe, out for world domination. They regard us as their obstacle. They are ultimately ready to use any means if that will achieve our defeat. If they were to be successful, they would impose a police state upon us which would take away all the oxygen in our air of freedom. The experience which we went through with the Nazis and Fascists during the 30's should have convinced us all that appeasement does not pay and that determined and united resistance is necessary to defend freedom. We are now faced with an equally evil but more skillful adversary and determined resistance should be central to all our thinking and to our acts. I am therefore *not* proposing that scientists should cease to develop the military uses of nuclear energy. On the contrary, this work must go forward.

I do ask, however, the engineers and scientists to work on the problem of how air contamination and radioactive fallout can be lessened whether by undeground, underwater, or stratospheric explosions and to carry on a program of popular enlightenment about these matters such as a very few have been doing. Certainly the scientists should try to build up an informed public opinion, not only within the free world but also within the neutral and iron curtain countries, of the dangers involved in atomic testing, of the degree to which the Soviet Union is responsible for this, and of the total destruction which total war would bring. This should not weaken our will to resist and to defend freedom but it should help to build up an informed public opinion all over the world to seek a more peaceful solution of the conflicts of our time.

In short, a free society has the right to expect its scientists and engineers to believe in freedom and to seek both to defend and enlarge it. This is to be a freedom for truth to be sifted from error by testing and by reason, to help set mankind increasingly free from excessive toil, prejudice, and passion. And in their leisure hours, I urge that they be skilled participants in movements to clean up our streams and waters from the increasing pollution, to provide adequate havens of rest and recreation, to help see to it that all communities have adequate school and library services, and that the intellectual and spiritual climate is favorable to open and tolerant discussion, to a consideration of issues upon their merits, and to the love for and practice of the joys both of pure thought and of artistic expression.

If one embarks upon this course then I predict that life will be both more interesting and more meaningful. Perhaps only a few will have the courage of the great Charles P. Steinmetz, the famous research director of the General Electric Company, who when he became chairman of the school board of Schenectady found that GE was not paying its fair share of the community's taxes and that the school children were suffering as a result. After thinking the matter over, Steinmetz arranged a series of community meetings at which he appeared and explained just what the facts were and then demanded that GE's tax assessments be increased more closely to their real value. It was a tribute to Steinmetz and the citizens of Schenectady that this was done. It is also something of a tribute to General Electric that they did not fire him, although his genius and general worth to them undoubtedly gave him a protection which men of lesser abilities would not have been accorded.

Lest it be thought that I exaggerate the need for scientists and engineers to be bold and creative thinkers and socially concerned citizens, let us soberly recognize the pressures which society seems to be increasingly imposing for an unthinking conformity. We are all acquainted with the type of "organization man" which is being evolved within our great corporations, our suburbs, and in our political and social organizations as well. This is the man who agrees with every dominant group or policy, and who conforms fully and exactly with the customs of those about him. Now, whatever may be our views and attitudes towards life, I believe nearly all of us would agree that in secular matters this type of attitude is distinctly *not* to be encouraged among the members of any group, and particularly not among educated men.

The world has progressed in large part because of the sense of curiosity and inquiry, coupled, of course, with a high sense of ethical responsibility. And it is this combination of qualities which we should seek to foster among our engineers and scientists as well as among our technicians. Colleges and universities should resist the drift to a deadening uniformity and encourage the creative and inquiring spirit. This attitude is perhaps one of the most important qualities which an educational institution can develop.

But lest I be misunderstood, I must immediately state certain qualifications to make my meaning more precise.

One should not make a convention of unconventionality and differ from prevailing customs just in order to be different. This I suspect is the intellectual error into which the young beatniks have rushed. The mere growing of a beard and the wearing of blue jeans and dirty sweaters are not desirable qualities in themselves, nor do they indicate any true originality of spirit. Nor is the embracing of unpopular political and social opinions necessarily a virtue in itself. What I am asking for is not blind and sentimental revolt but a considered, ordered and socially based independence of mind and spirit which gladly supports the good features of our society even as it seeks improvement.

Secondly, as I stressed earlier, while reason should have its dignified and proper place, the ethical and spiritual imperatives should be controlling. As Pascal wisely observed, "the heart has reasons which reason knows not of." It is my own faith that this imperative should be the desire to embody and to transmit the spirit of Christian love and to help create an ever broader fellowship bound together by love and good will. This, too, is a part of the education of the whole man which a free society should expect and try to provide.

And now may I add another note which to many may seem minor. Our scientists and technicians should also be cultured men who can cultivate the gardens of the mind and spirit. Technical competence in itself seems graceless. To raise life to its highest level of attraction there should be some cultivation of hobbies and some deep interests outside of one's work and one's duty as a citizen. The world has been a fascinating place for a long time and so it is today. The great masters of literature—Shakespeare, Goethe, Tolstoi—have plumbed the problems of human existence to the depths and to read them is to experience in a vicarious fashion the intensity and mystery of life. The Sistine Chapel is one of the glories of the world and the incomparable Michaelangelo who painted those breath-taking frescoes was probably the greatest artistic genius of the race. His paintings, his sculpture and the perfectly swelling dome of St. Peter's which he created are works to become acquainted with and to love. And how much richer our lives are for Bach, Mozart, and Beethoven and how close at hand they now are for us to hear and to enjoy. And nature outdoors beckons to us in lake and mountain, forest and plain, with a wealth of animate and inanimate life which we can enjoy and understand.

And what about the history of the human race itself, of the rise and fall of empires, the movements of thought, the formation and functioning of religious societies and the broadening ethical consciousness of man? Could anything be more commanding than these? And may we not be moved to reverence by such lives as St. Francis, St. Dominic, and St. Benedict, and by such modern embodiments of the true and the good as Albert Schweitzer and Jane Addams.

In short, to the educated man life should never be boring and despite the competitive struggle for excellence and for success there is now being provided sufficient leisure for the human spirit to expand.

The great engineers and scientists have always been more than mere technicians and as men have transcended their occupations. Pascal was a theologian as well as mathematician. Steinmetz was an accomplished organist, as is Albert Schweitzer. Herbert Hoover took a year off from his early career as a mining engineer to study Latin and to translate Agricola's work on mining and minerals. John Hays Hammond was a man of almost endless interests as is his talented son.

I am not asking that men should become dilettantes and neglect their work. Far from it. But life is long and its facets innumerable. As we go through life let us savor its richness as we pass. And youth is a good time in which to begin. This ability to experience the fullness of life must be imparted by example, rather than by formal discipline.

Dr. Frederick C. Lindvall

ON THE NATURE OF THE ENGINEER

THE engineer is known by his works and his objectives. Long before the word "engineer" came into the language, certain men designed and built the structures of the ancient world, the palaces, the temples, fortifications, roads and bridges. Fertile but arid lands were transformed by the miracle of irrigation into gardens for produce and for pleasure. Cities were made possible by water supplies brought from great distances in primitive aqueducts and were made livable by development of systems of waste disposal. The early engineer exploited water transport through canals, locks, and stream improvement and sought to control floods.

Gradually the ingenuity of man devised machines to replace human labor. The early engineer found new materials and new ways of improving old materials. His objective was to adapt nature to the needs and wants of mankind. But as he devised new schemes and new

Frederick C. Lindvall is professor of electrical and mechanical engineering at the California Institute of Technology.

machines, he was also asking the question, "Why?" He was curious and sought to understand the workings of nature not solely for projection to new applications, but as new knowledge itself. In his efforts to understand we recognize the beginnings of science. Indeed, many of these early investigators whom we now call "scientists" were first of all pragmatic, practical fellows with specific objectives not different from those of engineers. And experimental science, beginning as early as the thirteenth century and flowering in the seventeenth, adopted empirical experimental methods then used by engineers and artisans. "Engineering helped to stimulate the rise of modern science in the seventeenth century and was in turn changed in character by the birth of applied science in the nineteenth."[1]

Now mid-twentieth century technology is again working at the frontiers of knowledge. Engineers and scientists jointly are seeking new information and as a team are developing new applications. A new engineering development or new instrumentation brings to light unexpected facts which extend our knowledge in corroboration of existing theory or force re-examination of popular hypotheses.

"The point where technology leaves off and science begins—the distinction between applied and basic research—has become increasingly fuzzy. In the Sixties it will become fuzzier yet, for the great research tools that will dominate physical science in the years ahead will be engineering marvels first and research tools second."[2]

The teamwork is so close that a clear identification of the engineering and science functions is difficult, if indeed such identification is significant. Similarly, the nature of the engineer becomes less clear in our most advanced technological developments. He is not the boots and breeches engineer of hoary tradition; neither is he the white-coated scientist of Madison Avenue fiction. Is he, in fact, becoming an applied scientist or does he have distinctive attributes as an engineer? The

[1] R. S. Kirby, Sidney Withington, A. B. Darling, and F. G. Kilgour, *Engineering in History* (New York: McGraw-Hill, 1956), p. 126.
[2] Francis Bello, "The 1960's: A Forecast of the Technology," *Fortune*, LIX (January 1959), 194.

answer has more than casual significance for engineering as a profession and profound implications for engineering education.

Dr. James Killian in a recent talk in Detroit said: "We need also to bring more clearly into focus the image of the engineer in the minds of our citizens. Despite all the efforts of our engineering societies and councils, this image is not sharp or accurate. For example, the lack of any clear distinction between the scientist and engineer has been manifest in all the recent public discussions of our national strength in science and technology. Some of the great engineering accomplishments of our time have come to be loosely tagged, in the public mind, under the generic title of science. This confusion is not in the interest either of science or engineering, and the scientists are as unhappy about the confusion as the engineers."[3]

Let me also summarize the statement of another engineering college administrator, who expressed a general reaction: He feels strongly that one of the serious problems in getting qualified young people to go into engineering schools is the great stress today on science, —"with the almost total omission of painting the role of the engineer in society for the general public.—The development of nuclear power, the development of the atomic submarine, the development of satellites— are always spoken of as scientific achievements, when, of course, they are major engineering feats." Over the long-run, if we are to "draw into engineering education those students who are eminently fitted and who can make major contributions, we have a major educational job to do. This requires a well-conceived and well-executed continuing plan of painting an accurate picture of what the engineer does and the kind of liberal training for a modern technological society which our very best engineering schools provide."

Dr. Killian continues: "I do not advocate any less emphasis on science and its importance. I do urge a comparable emphasis on the role and importance of the engineer."[4]

[3] Remarks of Dr. James R. Killian, Jr. before The Economics Club of Detroit, February 23, 1959.
[4] *Ibid.*

The Science Advisory Board, of which Dr. Killian is Chairman, created a Panel to consider problems in Science and Engineering Education. This Panel has prepared a paper which attempts to define problem areas and proposes some recommendations. This paper will soon appear, but in the meantime, a preview of a few pertinent paragraphs will further illuminate the engineering identification.

"The *scientist* is one who seeks to extend the boundaries of knowledge in his chosen field. The *engineer* has the task of combining the knowledge of science with his knowledge and awareness of the needs and limitations of human beings and of a human society to develop and create new 'things' for human use. These things may vary from a tiny transistor to a huge dam, a hearing aid to a superhighway, an automobile, an airplane or a space vehicle. While the scientists have uncovered the basic knowledge, it is the engineers who have created the tangible tools, materials, and products that have revolutionized our daily lives, our community living and our national defense.

"The scientist and the engineer form the team that paces today's technology. In science lie the foundations upon which the engineer builds toward a goal of the utility, comfort and advancement of man. He is concerned with machines, the environment in which they operate, and with the men who work with them and effect their control. In the broad sense the engineer derives from fundamental science the principles, the material properties and the analyses from which he synthesizes the system which is to achieve the objective, produce the result, create the product which is sought. In short, the engineer is the member of the technological team who creatively adapts the findings and methods of science to meet the needs and desires of mankind. He is further distinguished from his colleagues in science in his constant concern to achieve an optimum design to meet the many and frequently conflicting criteria of performance, reliability, efficiency, cost and producibility. The associated synthesis, analysis and design of an element or a system are unique characteristics of engineering.

"The profession of engineering has thus become one of the most important in modern society. Our civilization would deteriorate, would become too weak to survive in modern world competition without the work of the hundreds of thousands of trained men (and the too few women) who keep the wheels of industry turning, who create new and useful products, who envisage, design, and build great factories, intricate communication, power and transportation systems, and vast irrigation, navigation and flood-control projects. The scientist and engineer have created for the first time in history a society potentially free from want—one more concerned, in fact, with surplus than with scarcity of many material products, as well as a society in which freedom from back-breaking toil has been largely achieved. Finally, in today's great international competition, America's ability or inability to help others in their engineering progress may be crucial.

"Clearly, the engineering profession offers unparalleled opportunities to the able young men and women of the country."[5]

I wish to return to the statement that the engineer is concerned with "machines, the environment in which they operate, and the men who work with them and effect their control." An example or two will help to identify the meanings of these words.

The electronic equipment of a modern fighter aircraft accomplishes various functions: navigation, communication, identification, radar search, fire control. A man is the nerve center, so to speak, of this electronic system, to receive and process information, and to take appropriate action. Yet only recently has this electronics package been designed as a complete system, in the modern sense of the word, taking into account the man and the environment. The environment includes such factors as temperature, humidity, pressure, stray electrical or magnetic fields, vibration, noise, light levels, visibility. The man must be presented with information clearly and simply, he must be able to perform control, adjustment, interpretation functions and finally take the necessary action to complete the mission which is the sole reason for the existence of the system. He has physical and mental limitations in speed of response, basic reaction times and so on, which the designer

[5] President's Science Advisory Board, *Education for the Age of Science,* (Washington, D.C.: U.S. Government Printing Office, 1959), 0-507988, pp. 21, 22.

must recognize in evaluating the overall effectiveness of the system. Insofar as possible, human limitations and fallibility should be bypassed and all needless distraction, inconvenience and clumsiness must be avoided in the presentation of data and arrangement of essential controls.

At the same time the human factor is being minimized and human skills reserved for those functions which cannot be performed by other means, the systems engineer seeks a minimum of equipment to meet performance specifications with acceptable reliability. An absolute minimum of equipment may be attractive in low cost, small weight, low power requirements, little space, simplicity. Yet with no duplication of critical functions reliability may be less than acceptable. Some degree of redundancy will improve reliability, but at the price of added weight, cost, complexity and so on. The engineer must balance these conflicting factors.

Nowhere are such conflicting requirements brought more clearly into focus than in the overall design of a commercial aircraft. This airplane is designed to provide fast, dependable transportation at a price which will make profits for its owners. The end objective is to maximize profits, commonly a corrolary to minimum operating costs, but not necessarily so if passengers or shippers will pay extra for a premium service.

The aircraft structures group would like to design the wings with considerable depth to simplify the structural problem. The aerodynamics group would like to have an extremely thin wing for best aerodynamic performance. The power plant group would like all the space possible in and on the wings for engine mounting and for fuel tanks, as well as exhaust ducts and provision for auxiliaries. The operating personnel would like as much radar, communication equipment and conveniences for safety and comfort. Pressurization and air conditioning constitute no small part of the problem of environment for passengers and crew. Yet somehow all of these conflicting and seemingly incompatible requirements must be brought together in a workable system which must meet the overall requirement of profitable operation.

Another example of the less glamorous but highly important system is an electrical power system with its interconnection of many generating stations and load centers. Here there are two controlling criteria: reliable service and minimum cost per kilowatt hour. Present utility systems are the result of many years of effort to achieve these criteria and indeed it is a noteworthy engineering accomplishment that despite rising costs and general inflationary trends, cost to the consumer of a kilowatt hour has stayed substantially constant. This is because engineers have been striving for higher and higher efficiency in the basic generating units and for improvements in the distribution system to minimize the problem of accidental outages. In the operation of the system wherever it is possible to do so, the individual generator units are carefully scheduled to give a good balance between Hydro generation and steam generation to take care of daily and seasonal load variations with the lowest possible unit energy cost.

Automation is a word which currently carries an aura of glamour, but it is not a new subject for those engineers who have been concerned with automatic machinery and its control for many years. It is only that the scope of automation is now so much greater and the possibilities have been enormously enlarged by the development of digital and analog computers. Not only do computers themselves form an integral part of some automation systems, many of the techniques and components of computers have found utility in simple applications. For example, punched or magnetic tape can now provide instructions to rather complex machines performing a variety of sequential and parallel operations, without the need of human attention other than casual supervision. The objectives of automation are in part production economy and saving of labor, but also in the shortening of overall time from initial design to production parts through elimination of some of the detailed drawings, templates and die work which non-automated machinery requires.

In all of these systems which have been cited to identify the meaning of a system and the scope of the engineer's work, some objective criteria are to be satisfied. That is, as stated earlier—the engineer "is further distinguished from his colleagues in science in his constant concern to achieve an optimum design to meet the many and frequently conflicting criteria of performance, reliability, efficiency, cost and producibility. The associated synthesis, analysis and design of an element or a system are unique characteristics of engineering."[6]

This identification of the engineer is intended to stress the design function, the creative effort and the objective weighing of alternatives which mark the good engineer and always have. Some 60 years ago A. M. Wellington, an engineer, wrote a book in which he discussed the problems of railway location.[7] To paraphrase Wellington, no matter how forbidding a region nor how many feasible routes there may be, one route exists which will be superior to all others in overall long-range cost, and it is the essence of good engineering to find that optimum solution. This statement could easily apply to present-day engineering systems, but the details are much more complex and cover a wider range of the physical sciences.

To what extent new methods of engineering analysis and synthesis will emerge to organize the work more formally is not clear. More important, however, is the possibility of doing a better job than we have in engineering education, in broad-scale thinking, systems engineering, design and operations research. To what extent these things are teachable is unknown. Creativity and judgment as such are not teachable; they depend upon inherent qualities in a student. However, *methods* of thinking, schemes of organization of parameters for systematic evaluation, and understanding of engineering objectives probably can be introduced successfully into formal engineering education. The morphological approach is one suggestion. More attention to careful statements of complex problems is another technique.

Engineering teachers must always be conscious of the fact that the purpose of engineering is not merely *analysis,* but *synthesis and*

---

6 *Ibid.*
7 *The Economic Theory of the Location of Railways* (New York: J. Wiley and Sons, 1887), p. 832.

design. Undoubtedly we will be able to present broader approaches to design—structural design is reasonably manageable—in which the power and speed of modern computers is used to study quickly the effect of many variables and choices and thus approach an optimum design with confidence. Some electric motors and transformers are now being designed in this way. The essential principles and an awareness of the method are vital for today's students to know. This is an important area for educational advance.

The engineer has the lively motivation of finding the best solution to a problem and as time goes on he has at his disposal new tools which allow him to analyze larger problems with more assurance. Analog and digital computers are rapidly becoming important design tools and it is possible to make synthetic solutions to problems and discover the effects of varying any of the many possible parameters which can effect the end result. Civil Engineering structures, for example, lend themselves well to computer techniques and give the engineer an opportunity to run quickly through several alternative designs to give the one which most nearly meets all of his design objectives. For example, an analysis of a concrete arch dam has recently been made with a digital computer and the engineers had the satisfaction of varying several important boundary conditions and constraints, a change in any one of which would have required several days more of desk type calculation. With the modern computer these changes required only minutes to make and only a few more minutes for the results. Computers, of course, are no substitute for the creative effort required in engineering synthesis and design. However, a variety of combinations and possibilities may be run through without pain and indeed it may happen that a combination of elements which had not been used before will be the best answer to a problem.

The engineer must first create a system or a device which he expects to be a reasonable solution to his problem. With this proposed solution, the engineer can then proceed to analyze it for its feasibility and possible performance. Depending upon circumstances, this analysis may be simple or complex. It may be that the analysis can be done through the medium of a mathematical model and thus readily be reducible to modern computer assistance. But this basic design calls for creative effort of a high order. Then as the analysis proceeds, modifications develop and a final configuration emerges. It may become apparent that essential information is lacking. Basic science has failed to give necessary information in ranges of temperature or stress or corrosive conditions which are inherent factors in the new design. Then the engineer must undertake to develop this new information for himself. He will then be working as a scientist and his work may be indistinguishable from that of the scientist as to technique or information sought. But he has a definite engineering objective. He knows why he needs the information, where he is going, and when he is expected to arrive with the finished design.

The engineer has always had to work without complete knowledge of his materials. One of our commonest materials, mild steel, has some peculiar properties which other steels and non-ferrous materials do not have. Among other properties, mild steel has the annoying one of fracturing in a brittle manner at moderately low temperatures. The temperature at which the nature of failure changes from plastic to brittle is called the "transition temperature," which describes but does not explain the effect. Certain recent work promises to yield an explanation, but in the meantime hundreds of annoying brittle failures have occurred because we do not know how to eliminate the transition or to push the transition temperature far below normal environmental temperatures.

And, as another example, the full explanation and understanding of semiconductor devices is only partially developed. However, this does not stop the engineer from the innumerable useful applications of these devices. In due time from solid state physics the complete understanding may come.

In some ways the engineer functions in the service of mankind the way the medical practitioner does. The recent development of polio vaccine is a good example. For some time basic research on the nature and behavior of the polio virus has been underway. Rather than wait until everything is known about the polio virus, Dr. Salk undertook the development of the vaccine which has had such dramatic and effective results in removing most of the curse of polio. The ironical fact seems to be that the public has now largely lost its fear of polio and has become careless in availing itself of the protection of the vaccine. Other medical examples could be cited to reinforce this analogy to certain features of engineering practice. In fact, some of the earlier definitions of the engineer which broadly said in effect—"he seeks to adapt the forces and properties of nature for the benefit of mankind"—could apply equally well to our medical colleagues.

But Engineering of today is clearly in a state of transition. New developments in science which have claimed the attention of scientists have left the engineer with large areas of what are called Classical Physics and Chemistry, which he must explore for himself if he wishes to develop the new knowledge he needs for application. Much of Physics has become the domain of the engineer. Some examples are: physical properties of materials at extended temperature, solid state physics, electricity and magnetism, physical electronics, theoretical mechanics, thermodynamics, spectroscopy, thermodynamic properties. The engineer has also become increasingly concerned with problems of chemistry, particularly reaction kinetics and combustion processes. The engineer today is also perhaps the most important contributor to applied mathematics and to computer logic and design.

We can look ahead and see many problem areas which will require engineering solutions. The space age is with us, presumably to stay. The design of vehicles is the province of the engineer experienced to understand obvious requirements for propulsion, guidance, control and communications. There are ramifications of the control and guidance which are highly speculative and arise from the desire to have vehicles which can move from one orbit to another. How shall this orbit power be obtained? From the sun? From chemical fuel carried with the vehicle? From nuclear sources? The engineer must make an evaluation for optimum performance hinging around the crucial points of necessary power and the penalty of weight. The engineer must also be intimately concerned with the problems of aviation medicine in order that he may create an environment in which the space voyagers may live and perform their functions.

Another whole new area of engineering concern is data handling and processing. Certain new systems for doing this have been created and have been spectacularly successful. Yet only a start has been made in the exploitation of the possibilities of data processing. Data handling and processing is of course an activity which will have even more important applications in the commercial and financial world than in engineering activities. Nevertheless, the design and the building of these systems will be the work of the engineer. He will be concerned with the sensing devices which make the basic measurements and obtain the basic data, the transmission of this information, the handling, sorting and processing of the data, the presentation of the results and the output devices which may be required for effecting controls. Flight testing of modern aircraft will be done with ground stations to which information will be transmitted from a minimum of airborne equipment in the aircraft in flight. A great deal more information will be collected in the airplane in a much shorter period of time than ever before. Everything about the modern aircraft happens so much faster and there is so much more information that the engineer needs to know to make it practical to obtain the flight records with a complete airborne system. In missiles the situation is even more acute. With the data handling and processing done in a ground station, there is the additional important advantage that in the event of failure and loss of the aircraft, all of the essential information up to the moment of faliure will be preserved to answer the all-important question "what was the cause of failure?"

Inherent in data handling and processing are the elements of Information Theory, which is itself rapidly emerging as an engineering discipline. In large measure Information Theory has been associated with Electrical Communication, but many of the basic principles and important generalizations are applicable to any system—mechanical, hydraulic, or electrical—which makes measurements, transmits the information and processes the data.

Energy conversion is assuming greater and greater importance. Considering electrical power systems alone, we have in the United States a total generating capacity of nearly one kilowatt per person and this is a point on a curve which has shown a doubling approximately every ten years. But, in addition to conventional energy conversion, ideas are beginning to emerge which are based on nuclear reaction, fission now and fusion a little later, on fuel cells which make direct chemical conversion, with energy release not limited by thermodynamic temperature considerations, and on radiation, solar or other. Fuel cells of efficiency comparable with that of a modern thermoelectric station could change radically the complexion of our public utility systems in terms of generation and distribution. It is not fanciful to think of automobiles powered by fuel cells and electric motors. Indeed one of the automotive research laboratories has mentioned this dream car.

Materials are for the engineer both a handicap and a challenge. "If," as one writer maintains, "any one factor were to be singled out as holding back progress in atomic power and other advanced technologies, it would be lack of suitable engineering materials— particularly, metals and alloys. The materials situation is regarded as so serious that a number of worried scientists are urging that the government establish a major new research institute wholly devoted to the problem. . . . The problem in metallurgy is easy to state: there has as yet been no major breakthrough in metals comparable to the transistor in electronics, nylon in high polymers, or nuclear fission in energy creation."[8]

Clearly, the engineer of the future has opportunities and responsibilities beyond those which we know today. His capabilities in science, in analysis and in design call for continuing professional development. Furthermore, the sophistication of the components and the complexity of the systems with which the engineer must work will call

[8] Bello, *op. cit.,* p. 192.

for educational effort which goes beyond the present, if he is to function as a truly professional man.

Then in addition to the greater understanding of modern science and the synthesis of knowledge into engineering systems, a third func tion of the engineer is growing in importance. This is his management and technical leadership function. His education must include sub-stantial work in the humanities and the social sciences, this in addition to facility in communicating his ideas and understanding those of others. The repeated plea from industry that engineers should have such breadth, leaves no doubt concerning the importance of the humanities. Furthermore, we are urged as Educators to omit practical training such as labor relations, personnel management, and similar things which have little meaning for the young graduate and which industry can supply more effectively later when motivation exists. In short, industry believes it can do a better job than colleges can in giving supervisory or management training, but that the colleges can function better in their traditional role of education in the broad social-humanistic areas. Also, in the broader sense, engineers have come to value the humani-ties as fundamental to understanding man in his social environment. The engineer thus recognizes his growing professional responsibility.

Now comes the important question—can the necessary basic sci-ence, the engineering sciences, synthesis and design, and the humanities be fitted into a four year program? In a superficial way, yes, but not with the level of comprehension needed for tomorrow's work. Everything points to the necessity for more extensive education than is possible in a four year B.S. program. More graduate work will be essential for the engineering leaders of the future; the pressure for it is evident now. The objective must be an education which will have the breadth to permit broad-scale systems thinking and at the same time have sufficient depth to permit the necessary specialization. Then, who designs the hardware?

Mr. Luke Noggle of the Westinghouse Company has written: "You may ask—This science education is fine, but who is going to design the hardware? There is emerging a new type of educational institution which expects to train personnel to handle this type of work. These schools are engineering-oriented technical institutes and feature a two year terminal program. Such programs comprise specialized courses which prepare the student for a particular technology. Since these programs are for only two years' duration, naturally much of the instruction is directed toward a particular field as industrial control, electronics, power and radio engineering. The student's preparation is up-to-date in these technologies and the course content in the applied sciences approaches an equivalent of a B.E. degree earned ten to fifteen years ago. It is possible to find some of these schools teaching the application of differential equations in circuit analysis, the use of vector analysis in field theory and the use of LaPlace Transformations in transients. These are exceptions, but most of the accredited technical institutes offer course work using the applications of differential and integral calculus. The graduates from these schools could easily, with practical training and experience, be placed in many positions which are normally reserved for the college graduates in engineering."[9]

Our colleagues in Science have never regarded the Bachelor's degree as anything but a good start. The real professional education came in graduate work. Engineering is rapidly approaching this state. It is also clear that the engineering art and practice does not belong in college instruction, but is knowledge which industry should expect to provide. The college responsibility, in turn, should be for more intensive education, extending beyond our conventional four years, including greater emphasis on creative design and the synthesis of more comprehensive systems. The engineer of the future will thus be better educated not only in science, but in the distinctive elements of engineering. He will have adequate supporting personnel working with him as part of the technical team. He will thus be able to function in truly professional capacity, to adapt creatively, in optimum fashion, the findings and methods of science to meet the needs and desires of mankind.

[9] *Criteria for the Selection of Engineers for Employment,* A Report to the 1959 AIEE Winter General Meeting, (CP No. 59-418), p. 5.

Dr. Dumont F. Kenny

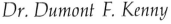

CONFERENCE SUMMARY PANEL—I

WE HAVE demonstrated that one of the real benefits of this conference was the bringing together of people from the sciences and the humanities in the interests of communication, leading hopefully to the confrontation and clarification of ideas and problems of mutual concern. To have persons here concerned with knowledge for the sake of knowledge and at the same time to have others concerned with knowledge for the sake of doing or making — that is, action or art — is a necessary and a helpful thing. I would like to express this word of personal appreciation to those at Marquette University for making this possible. I would witness that there have been gains to each of us professionally from the experience.

It is a refreshing and encouraging thing to have a physical scientist such as Dr. Teller tell us that good scientists are strange fellows. *But aren't we all?* His insight, it seems to me, is the fact

Dumont F. Kenny is Vice-President for Program Development, National Conference of Christians and Jews that difficulty and diversity are a test of the free society. Secondly, his conception of science as fun was picked up and echoed by all scientists here, even if redefined as personal appreciation or personal satisfaction. Perhaps, if this consensus is timely, the walls which we have been building between the sciences and the arts are a little bit too high or a little bit too arbitrary. The impersonal character of science, we have been saying to each other over the years, makes it fundamentally different from the arts, from the humanities. This is of course true in important respects. But is there not also a place for merely differences of degree? For example, if we encounter everywhere in science what Einstein called the pre-established harmonies, is this not also a field where the artist has some concern and appreciation? I think it is.

Necessary considerations from the fields of scientific education and humanistic education needed to be brought in here and it was helpful to have this area opened up by Father Weigel. A scientist is a human being before he is a scientist, he observed, and he should develop his humanity no less than his scientific sense. Appropriately, I feel, the discussion of his topic, "What Does Religion Demand of the Scientifically Educated," set up rather early the converse relationship of what do the scientifically educated demand of religion. Although these propositions tended to be set up as contradictories, and somewhat in opposition, I would suggest that this kind of relationship can be extremely productive if we attempt to put ourselves in the place of our opposite numbers with some appreciation for their tasks. It is true that religion would demand certain things from the scientifically educated. Testimony given in the discussion as to the beauty and order of the universe or to the teleological makeup of cells is really religious witness. Conversely, I think that the scientist could rightfully expect that the work of the clergyman become relevant and meaningful to his type of problems. After all, the task of our clergy is the reformulation of eternal truths in terms that make sense and are directly appropriate to the human temporal situation.

This is no small task, yet appreciation on both sides can, I think, give us the dialogue needed for mutual advance.

The role of expert and expert knowledge were important recurring considerations and opened up some of the important things that needed to be said, especially in terms of the scientist in a free society. One or two points, however, might still be registered in this area. Since both science and democracy have grown up together during the same period it is perhaps inevitable that the tempting analogies of scientific and democratic process would be attractive to many seeking means for arriving at an agreement concerning the vexing and urgent problems discussed. Yet, attempts to make democracy scientific or science democratic help neither science nor democracy. Clarity is needed. The differences between scientific and political roles noted in the discussions need to be articulated in wider arenas. Scientific method is never wholly adequate for the solution of practical problems and social policy decisions. One may indeed solve a social problem in a sense of figuring out how conditions may be changed for the better, yet there is still the problem of getting the proposed remedies actually effected. In fact, as the discussion brought out so well, the habits of mind that solve a scientific problem are different from the modes of discourse and the dramatic appeal necessary to change a social condition. Politicians may indeed regulate science and scientists may determine policies, but when they do, they confuse the functions of knowledge in resolving problems and in inducing belief and action. The task of the scientist, it seems to me, is research for the acquisition of knowledge. The task of a statesman or politician is invention for the guidance of action.

How to get in a free and abundant society sufficient motivation and the right kind of motivation for science education was, in Dr. Teller's formulation, a crucial problem of the conference. Difficulties and failures assessed in the discussion tended, in my opinion, to rest on too narrow a basis. Blame was placed by some primarily on the schools. I don't think this is quite fair. If we worry about the necessary motivation for science education, don't we have to go a step further and look at the basic value structures which predominate in our society in the year 1959? Is there not something wrong in that value structure when the person who in other ages was the court entertainer now receives top income while those entrusted with the intellectual and moral education of the young of the nation are down on the bottom of the scale? If the order is subverted, how can we expect our teachers and our formal educational institutions to do anything but reflect in some measure the basic values predominant in this society.

The task is one that has to be approached on a broader front than just formal education. I would suggest that one way of securing this motivation is to take cognizance of and to use the existing social institutions which do so much to make all of us what we are in terms of our attitudes and practices. An effective and economical way to increase this motivation on the part of citizens who are not scientists is to work with and through the varying social institutions of our churches, schools, community organizations, labor-management organizations, and media of mass communication.

On the other hand, the scientist, it seems to me, since he is also a citizen, must continue his education in citizenship and the humanities in these informal ways as well. To a person who has dealt with the precision and niceties of physical science it may be a bit repugnant to come face to face with the untidy compartments of practical affairs. Yet, to immerse oneself in the organizations and institutions which must cope with these untied and slippery areas of human life is an inescapable responsibility. The sobering thought to buttress this point is the simple fact that our major problems today really are not in the area of man's relation to the physical universe but in the area of man's relationship to man.

These relationships are a disgrace and have a direct bearing on our concerns professionally. Breakdowns in human relationships are page one news from South Carolina to South Africa, and if we look at the international aspects of this problem, we are reminded by Norman Cousins, the editor of the *Saturday Review,* that in over 5,000 years of recorded history we have only had something like 292 years of peace. In the new world being opened by the advances of science and technology we stand either on the threshold of undreamed of human potentialities or a mere extension into outer space of the age-old suspicions, fears, hates, and prejudices which have dogged the footsteps of man as long as history has been written. The physical scientists here have helped make a contribution to the betterment of mankind which has been tremendous actually and potentially. It is now up to those of us in the fields of humanistic studies and practical affairs in relevant and appealing and persuasive ways to begin to match their technical know-how with a little more moral know-why.

Dr. Simon Ostrach

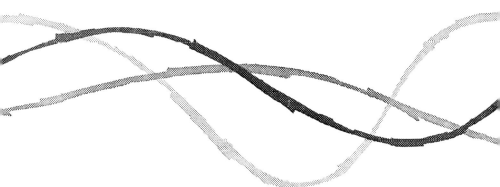

CONFERENCE SUMMARY PANEL—II

FIRST OF ALL, I would like to say that it has been a singular pleasure for me to have been part of this stimulating conference. The main lectures and many hours of discussion have been most provocative and significant. The fact that the convocator of this conference is a college of engineering not only attests to the maturity of that college but offers great promise for the future.

I hope, however, that you will not consider me too presumptuous if, as a member of this summary panel, I do not dwell too much on what has been said but rather indicate some of the important matters which have not been considered. An analysis of the reasons for the omission of these important questions would be interesting in itself. I am taking this somewhat perverse viewpoint in the hope of generating some thought and discussion on these problems which I pose not only from my own concerns but also from the writings of

Simon Ostrach is Chief, Fluid Physics Branch, National
Aeronautics and Space Administration.

other authors. Perhaps in this way the primacy which I assign to these questions can be verified or moderated for me.

One of the most striking aspects of this conference to me is the fact that we have all assembled here from so many disciplines and backgrounds with what seems to me to be a number of implicit fundamental assumptions. For example, I came here expecting that we would discuss somewhat the question of whether science alone is sufficient for guidance of human activities in this modern technological age. This is certainly the attitude which prevailed, at times passively and at times actively, throughout my own undergraduate and graduate education and is currently expressed vocally and in print by many seemingly responsible people. Yet here we have professors, scientists, engineers, and educators and the question was not even raised. I wonder, therefore, whether this was merely an oversight or were we, for whatever reasons, reluctant to pose this question, or is it that we here are all agreed that science alone is not enough.

Secondly, a great hue and cry was brought about in the educational world by the launching of the Russian Sputnik which has had proponents of the humanities and sciences at each others throats fighting for educational time. Once again we found absolutely none of this here. All the scientists seem to be ready and willing to add humanities to the curriculum, and all the humanists seem to be eager that students have more science training. This attitude on the part of both groups is, of course, good, but I wonder if this is merely a coincidence that we who have assembled here are all in agreement on these rather basic premises.

I was also quite surprised to find that, for the most part, the general tone of the discussions was quite sedate. I judge the conference subject and, in fact, our times to be most unique. All human activity has been greatly altered in the past decade and a half because of the rapid scientific and technological advances. Sociological problems have changed; our political and economic affairs are vastly different. There must be a great dynamicism shown to cope with these new situations. Perhaps all of this too is implicit in our thinking and there is no necessity of my bringing it up. However in my encounters with numerous people who are gravely concerned with the state of mankind, I am certain that they are not so clear in their minds of the true impact of science on human activity.

An awareness of this enormous effect of science on civilization and a responsibility for its direction must be explicitly imparted to the scientist and engineer in a free society. For some reasons, however, we sat there and talked about enriching and fulfilling each man's life just as if we were not living in unusual times of great change in which there is a question whether man will even survive. Although I will readily admit that the enrichment and satisfaction of each individual are desirable and necessary and perhaps are the very elements which were not stressed by our educational systems so that we are today confronted with our present dilemma, I do feel a greater sense of urgency than seemed to have been exhibited here.

The very uniqueness of our times should give us a strong incentive to make things better and to make them better in a hurry. The motivations for such actions, it seems to me, must, therefore, come from universal goals and ideals which can supercede the incentives based on personal satisfaction and fulfillment. This last assertion implies, of course, that religion must play an important role in the life of man today and indeed I believe that it must be the source of inspiration to which the free world must turn. In other countries less fortunate than ours today (as, in fact, was the case in the early days of our country's development) man is driven by hardship, grief, and tragedy to do good not only for himself but also for others. Science and technology are the means by which these ends are to be attained and the Soviet Union is employing those means to their fullest advantage not only to her own people but to many others throughout the world. This and not nuclear war represents the great threat to the free world for if Russia can significantly improve the lot of vast multitudes of people in the world, they will accept her ideology and man will lose his freedom.

Here in the United States where we have so many material and physical comforts we have lost a great deal of our earlier concern for the betterment of man and, consequently, not only has science suffered but also the cause of freedom is on the verge of feeling the impact of this complacency. If we do not want to regress to the point where personal suffering will again supply the spark to rekindle our efforts in behalf of a free civilization we will have to find our inspiration from another source and religion can be that source. I, therefore, feel that religious education must be an important part of every man's background and especially so for the scientist and engineer in a free society.

The final point which I would like to make is related to some of this afternoon's discussion on which I did not have the opportunity to comment. There seemed to be a rather strong feeling that the universities today should continue to give facts to the science and engineering students. Although certain facts are undoubtedly essential I wonder whether this is what should or can really be done. Scientific knowledge is increasing at such a tremendous rate that it seems almost impossible to do this any longer. I rather think that general formulations of fundamental concepts and ideas should be made clear and then the emphasis should be placed on deepening a student's insights for, after all, to paraphrase a favorite definition (whose originator escapes me) "education is what is left after one forgets what he learns." Young people should in the course of their formal education be made aware of the great problems in the world and be given indications of the great ideas which exist so that they will have some basis for their future thinking and work. This can be done by teaching science as a humanity and incorporating into the humanities the methods, ideas, and techniques of science.

L. E. Saline

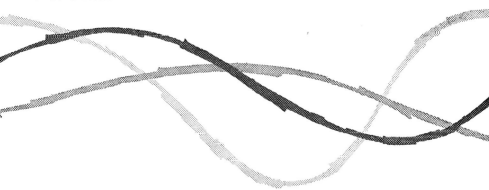

CONFERENCE SUMMARY PANEL—III

I WOULD like to take a slightly different tack than the other discussants and go back to the theme of the conference "the education of the scientist in a free society" and examine a few of the notions that are contained in that title. Next, I should like to reiterate some of the problems that have been brought up here earlier; and, perhaps add a few problems that have not been faced so far in the discussion.

First of all, what do we mean by a free society? In my concept, a free society is one in which people have both the opportunity and the responsibility for acting in a manner consistent with Biblical precepts. This is my definition. I don't apologize for it, I merely say that this is my general overall concept of free society.

The next thing I would like to touch on is my own meaning of scientific education. From my point of view, it embraces two general notions. One is that of technical proficiency, the second is that

L. E. Saline is Manager, Operations Analysis,
General Electric Company.

of social responsibility. Under technical proficiency, I would list two parts: first, subject matter and technical understanding; the second part comprises methodologies involved, problem recognition, problem solution, and good study habits.

The second area, social responsibilities, can be subdivided into three parts. First, appreciation of the humanities as they relate to our fellowmen; second, a desire to keep abreast of and to practice the humanities; and third, the developing of an understanding and tolerance of other points of view. These, I believe, to be goals of a scientific education.

The next subject I would like to examine very briefly is what I believe to be the various important parts of the educational process. First and fundamental is the home; second is elementary and secondary education; third is university education; fourth is the experiences one encounters after graduation, his associations with industry, with government, or with an educational institution; and fifth, overriding and intertwined among these other four, is one's own personal responsibility and contribution to educational progress.

I think it would be helpful to relate the responsibility for these five factors with what constitutes scientific education.

I am not going to do this in detail since it has been done in part already in the conference. I would like to emphasize, however, that we have almost meticulously avoided facing certain of these problems. We have touched, for example, on the role of the home in encouraging scientific interests early in life. Earlier in the conference, in our very extensive talk about religion, we almost entirely neglected the role of the home as far as religious development is concerned.

Again, this may have been a tacit assumption of everyone, but I find in my travels around the country and talks with many young folks and parents too that the role of the home is the factor omitted from our very important social life in this country. I find, too, that parents are very willing to pay their taxes and to assume that other people will assume their parental duties of raising children to be good citizens in a free society. I think this is an abominable curse on society today and all of us must recognize the important role of the home in this particular educational process.

I think we touched most extensively on the elementary and secondary educational institutions and their role in developing good scientists, but we failed to discuss extensively the role of the university in respect to the pedagogic techniques that should be used, for example, in graduate school.

We talked about curriculum but we didn't delve into the problems that graduate schools are facing today in the development of scientists and other technical people. We avoided completely the role of industry, government, and educational institutions in creating the environment and motivation for people to continue their education after they once leave the formal educational channels that we associate with formal educational institutions.

You have already heard in the discussion periods some of my answers which may or may not have been well received. I do not apologize for them at all. I talk as an engineer expressing very simple ideas which are very practical from several points of view.

I would like to review various problems as I see them which we are facing in the general subjects that have been discussed here during the conference. Obviously you will recognize many of these as originating from other participants, and for which I do not take credit. I will merely list some of these problems as I see them.

First of all, there is a real basic problem in identifying an individual's capabilities at an early age. Here I would like to stress that I am not referring to the identification of an individual's scientific capabilities. I am referring to capabilities in the broadest sense so that all individuals would get an opportunity to contribute where they can contribute best. I personally believe that if we do this, engineering and science and technology will get its fair share of all of the great human potential that is available.

Second, as was brought out by Dr. Teller, there is a real problem in creating proper home environment for the pursuit of science. Even more fundamentally, I believe that there is a real problem in creating proper home environment for the humanities including religion. I am sure all of us could contribute more in creating and showing by example the religious and other precepts that would be conducive to establishing some of the practices of individuals that would relate to and aid in their professional lives and careers.

Third, it has been well recognized that developing teachers and improving pedagogic techniques are fundamental problems. This is not only the method one uses to teach, but how one rewards teachers and all the other different ramifications of this general problem.

Fourth, there is a real problem of motivation of students. Dr. Ostrach has pointed this out to a degree, and I think this is really a serious problem. Serious consideration should be given to methods of motivating people with good capabilities not only in the field of science but in any field in which they have capabilities thus enabling them to achieve the utmost of their potential.

Fifth, I believe that the previously discussed problem of developing a balanced curricula within the available time for formal education is a real fundamental problem. I know that professional engineering education societies and other technical groups are giving considerable thought to this problem.

Sixth, I believe that instilling professional attitudes in students is a major problem that we must face if our educational objectives in science and technology are to be met successfully. For those who are not engineers, I would like to read the preamble to the Canons of Ethics for Engineers. I think it answers, to a degree, many of the things that were being discussed earlier in the conference. This statement of ethics applies particularly to the right attitude an individual should possess in evaluating the pressing problems that he might face in his professional career.

> Honesty, justice, and courtesy form a moral philosophy, which associated with mutual interest among men constitutes the foundations of ethics. The engineer should recognize such a standard not in passive observation but as a set of dynamic principles guiding his conduct and way of life. It is his duty

to practice his profession according to these Canons of Ethics. As the keystone of professional conduct . . . the engineer will discharge his duties with fidelity to the public, his employer, and clients and with fairness and impartiality to all.

It is his duty to interest himself in public welfare and to be ready to apply his special knowledge for the benefit of mankind. He should uphold the honor and dignity of his profession and also avoid association with any enterprise of questionable character. In his dealings with fellow engineers, he should be fair and tolerant.

I think that all of us would agree that if we could come to achieving the practice outlined in this preamble that we would have achieved a great deal toward establishing the right kind of moral attitudes amongst our technical people.

Dr. Teller has previously mentioned the seventh problem which is creating a social environment for optimum scientific contribution.

Eighth is the problem of developing within the individual student the study habits and discipline that will carry him along through his professional life. Such virtues will prevent his being stymied later in life because he had not been exposed to some situation in his formal college training.

Ninth is the need to encourage individuals in the practice and understanding of their religious beliefs and those of others. I personally believe that this is far more important than teaching people more religious literacy. I think the real crux of the problem is not to be more intellectually inclined and conversant about religion, but to practice those precepts that many of us are aware of and those we believe.

Tenth, a very knotty problem that has received no consideration formally by the group is, how do we pay for this kind of education?

Eleventh is the necessity of helping industry, government, and educational institutions understand their role in the education of scientists in a free society. Industry and government are playing deeper and deeper roles in education, and as you know, they are criticized by many educational institutions; but substitutions for their efforts have not been forthcoming and they will have a great influence on the education of scientists and technical people in the years to come.

The last problem is simply teaching the individual basic, fundamental laws and technical concepts that will be useful to him for a long period of time. These are the concepts and laws that will be useful not only six months after he graduates but those that will enable him to tackle the technical problems that he may face ten, fifteen, or twenty years after he leaves the technical institution. It is rather sobering for technical people to realize that people who are graduating in 1959 may be solving or contributing deeply to the solution of problems in the year 2000. Not only is it a sobering thought, but it is a fact of life. We should be sure that while we are providing the broadness and breath which people can depend on for right action in society we are not overlooking the very important role of all technical education which is to supply the people with the technical understanding and tools necessary for them to solve the undefined, unknown, and unnamed technical problems that are around the corner of tomorrow's work.

Finally, regardless of the number of problems that have been presented and discussed, I am very optimistic. We probably faced these problems thirty years ago and fifteen years ago. I know we faced them five years ago. The same problems will be reiterated in another five, ten, or twenty-five years. We have many problems to solve, but to this point we have come a long way in solving them. I think if we all continue to give our attention to them by making ourselves constantly aware of the problems, the future will continue to look pretty rosy.

Kurt F. Wendt

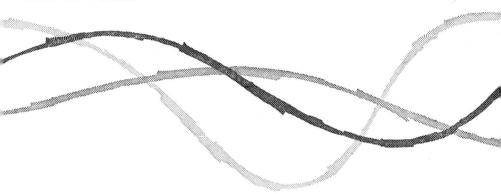

CONFERENCE SUMMARY PANEL—IV

I HAVE approached this assignment from a slightly different point of view than any of the other three discussants. It seems to me that there has been a certain amount of confusion during this discussion between the engineer, or engineering, and the scientist, or science.

Perhaps if we had the benefit of Dr. Lindvall's presentation of this evening, some of the remarks might not now be necessary because I think he will throw a good deal of light on the subject.

I think we should try, however, to define this relationship to a limited degree, and I choose to do it by looking at what I consider to be the general pattern of science and engineering development in the world in which we live. Starting with fundamental studies, which are called basic science or basic research, we find that they lead and grow directly into applied research. This in turn feeds into develop-

Kurt F. Wendt is Dean, College of Engineering,
University of Wisconsin.

ment, design, then production, and finally to the user or consumer via the sales route. This is a chain with, however, a great deal of feedback. While basic science feeds into applied science, applied science also feeds a great deal into basic science. Development often produces new and improved tools for basic and applied science, and even the user feeds back all the way to basic science by his questioning and his demands.

Where does the scientist begin and end? Where does the engineer begin and end? I think you will find a tremendous overlap and interdependence. There is no hard and fast line between basic and applied science. As far as I am concerned, science and engineering are so inextricably bound together that you must treat them more or less as a unit. We recognize that science begins with a search for knowledge, for the sake of knowledge, but does not stop there, and that engineering appears to be primarily concerned with the application of knowledge through the development of new devices and new systems. We must also recognize that the engineer constantly must reach back beyond the beginning of applied science into basic science for many concepts so that he is in fact doing scientific work at one end of the spectrum. In the same way the scientist is often doing application work at the other end of the spectrum.

Together science and engineering have made some notable contributions, as Dr. Kenney has indicated. Really, they have shaped society as we know it today to such a high degree that certain conclusions seem inevitable.

May I give you just one or two illustrations. You can think back, most of you, far enough so that you can appreciate the change in the social structure that has taken place because of the contributions of the scientists and the engineers. Every one of you recognizes the "shrinking" of the world because of the change in transportation. Most of you can think back almost to the inception of the automobile, certainly to the beginning of the airplane, and without doubt to jet propulsion. You can all think back to the beginning of communication as we know it today. Television is very, very recent and short or microwave technology is in its infancy. All of these have tended to shrink the world, to bring us all closer together, to make many of our problems our common concern.

The mobility of the population, the speed with which we can travel, the communications which we have established have changed the entire pattern of living in this country. No longer do we have to congregate in one place in order to do business. We are blessed or cursed, as you look at it, with the problem of what some people call "suburbia." This is a social scientist's problem, I suppose, but nevertheless, it is an outgrowth of these developments.

The tremendous contributions of science and engineering in providing pure water supplies and effective sewage disposal mean that a very large number of you gentlemen sitting around this table are here today instead of being long since dead. The life span has been essentially doubled in the last one hundred years in this country through such contributions coupled with the contributions of medicine.

All I am trying to get across is that the many contributions of science and engineering technology to our comfort, to our enjoyment, and to our "progress" have created a vast impact on the entire social structure of this country and every other country.

Most of these contributions are accepted without a second thought by the total population. If something is mechanical, if it is electrical, if it is wrapped up in a package, it must be good. Do you question or even stop to think when you buy a new automobile whether it is technically satisfactory, whether it is entirely safe, whether it will perform the way you think it is going to perform? Do you ever do any checking about these things? No, you accept them. You step into an automobile, turn the key and start down the road. You step on the brake and you expect the automobile to stop. It does, normally. You come to a corner and you turn the wheel and you expect the automobile to make the curve. It does, normally. People don't think about these things; they accept them. The work of the scientist, the work of the engineer, has been accepted broadly and completely. I could give you a thousand illustrations along this line.

Some other works of the scientist and engineer are being questioned, however, not because the things they have produced have not worked, but because of the way in which the knowledge and ideas they have developed are being applied. Nuclear power is one example. There seems to be some desire, whether this is real and conscious or whether it is unconscious, to shift the burden of decision and responsibility for the use of new knowledge from the user (and the user was defined during the course of this conference pretty much as the people, as represented by government at all levels) back to the scientist and the engineer.

Dr. Kenney covered this point in part. He said that the engineer and the scientist had made very large contributions, but that there were many agencies at work and we needed to work through all the agencies in order to make the best use of these contributions. He indicated that the real job was now up to the humanities. Recognition of the contributions of science and engineering is a great compliment, but no one person or related group of persons can encompass all of knowledge or effectively exercise the body of controls which would in fact determine the future of society. This has to be a collective effort. It has to be part and parcel not only of science and engineering, but also of government, politics, and religion. What, then, is the answer?

This conference is entitled "The Education of the Scientist in a Free Society." I think we have been talking about something else. I think the title should be "The Education of the Individual in a Free Society." We have been talking more about this than about the education of the scientist. In fact, we have pointed up first and foremost the very high degree of interdependence that exists in the world today between all people, between all disciplines. Having pointed up that high degree of interdependence it is obvious, and this need has been cited repeatedly, that we must have understanding.

Dr. Ostrach called it a deepening of insight. Others have characterized it in other ways. Father Weigel expressed it about as follows: "There is need for an appreciation of the dimensions of the several disciplines. There are many approaches to reality and truth with each area creating its own working model or map, none of which in itself is perfect, but each of which is helpful in understanding the other fellow's approach to the truth." This is really a plea for understanding, and this is what we must have above all.

Now, if we need understanding, we must also have respect. Again Father Weigel's statement might underline this need for respect. Simply because you don't understand the other fellow doesn't mean that he is talking nonsense. It doesn't mean that he knows not whereof he speaks or that he is wrong. We must respect other people's opinions and their accomplishments, and we must work with them. This is the basis of understanding.

To gain understanding and respect we also need communication — real communication — person to person — discipline to discipline. We have been spending most of our time on these needs — understanding, respect, and communication.

How do we begin to meet these needs? I have set down four or five points. Some of these have been stressed, others have been barely mentioned in passing. Certainly they are not in the order in which they were mentioned, nor necessarily in the order of importance, but the first I have is more work, and I emphasize the word work: more work in primary and high schools, longer hours, longer school years, harder work in the classrooms, more tasks and assignments, greater discipline, increased mental discipline. It appears a fact that we could make much more efficient use of time in the primary and secondary schools.

A second point that barely was touched is greater encouragement and support for the superior student at the primary and secondary levels as well as at the higher educational levels. If time permits exploration of this point in some depth, Dr. Clyde Brown could lead the discussion. He is devoting his time exclusively to this particular portion of the important problem that is before us. We can and must do a great deal more in this area. I pointed out this morning that the college senior would be in about the upper five per cent in ability for his age level. However, when I talk about the superior student, I mean the top two or three per cent of those college seniors, because it is from these truly exceptional and superior minds that we can expect new and imaginative approaches to complex problems and our greatest contributions.

Third is greater respect and tangible appreciation of teachers at all levels. This has been emphasized enough so I don't have to reiterate at length. Reward is important, and so are respect and esteem if we are to accomplish needed improvements in our educational system.

The fourth point which has been mentioned again and again, and runs through every one of the talks that has been given, is the need for appreciation of other disciplines to a much greater degree than at the present time. Such appreciation must be promoted by direct means — and we did have some major disagreements about the efficiency of doing the job — and by indirect means. Here I believe we have reached some degree of accord. We seemed to agree that it is incumbent upon each individual in a society such as ours to continue to study, to continue to educate himself broadly. This is the indirect means which must be encouraged. Dr. Teller in his talk and in the ensuing discussion was pleading for an atmosphere where science is appreciated and understood, and the creation of an atmosphere for cultural development. He concluded that separation of our intellectual disciplines one from another is disastrous.

Finally, it was agreed that each of us must strive to create a climate for cultural development that will lead to richer lives for all of us. Father Weigel's talk was a plea for cultural development in its broadest sense. Senator Douglas pointed out that cultural development is desirable, even though not mandatory, for the scientist.

His closing plea was for the creation of a climate for cultural development.

Understanding, respect, and communication one with another—if we recognize these as needs and take effective steps to promote them, and if we proceed to create a climate for cultural development, then we can be having, as Dr. Teller said, "fun in doing these things, a real and deep and abiding personal satisfaction in the kinds of lives that we are living."